A Future for Game?

A Future for Game?

Colin Laurie McKelvie

Foreword by
HRH the Duke of Edinburgh

Illustrations by
Charles Jardine

London
George Allen & Unwin
Boston   Sydney

George Allen & Unwin (Publishers) Ltd,
40 Museum Street, London WC1A 1LU, UK

George Allen & Unwin (Publishers) Ltd,
Park Lane, Hemel Hempstead, Herts HP2 4TE, UK

Allen & Unwin Inc.,
8 Winchester Place, Winchester, Mass. 01890, USA

George Allen & Unwin Australia Pty Ltd,
8 Napier Street, North Sydney, NSW 2060, Australia

George Allen & Unwin with the
Port Nicholson Press
PO Box 11-838 Wellington, New Zealand

First published in 1985

ISBN 0 04 799030 9

Set in 11 on 13 point Palatino
by Bedford Typesetters Ltd,
and printed in Great Britain
by Butler & Tanner Ltd, Frome and London

To
James Hamilton
of Brownhall

Contents

Contents

Foreword by
HRH The Duke of Edinburgh

The birds, mammals and fish that have come to be known as 'game' are part of the very fabric of British rural traditions. Very early in our history people realised that if these species were to continue to be available as economic and sporting assets they would need to be given the space and the opportunity to breed a surplus for the following year. The face of the countryside we know today was largely moulded by the enlightened self-interest of previous generations of landowners and sportsmen – although it must be said that, at times, enthusiasm for the control of predators did become excessive.

The industrial revolution, which fuelled the human population explosion, and the subsequent scientific revolution have put intolerable burdens on wildlife all over the world. The rate of extinction is rising every year, and the threat of extinction hangs over some of the world's most familiar species.

This important book raises the question whether there is any future for the game species in this country. It seems unthinkable that these familiar animals are slowly being forced out of existence by human selfishness and greed. Sadly this is a very real danger and if we fail to make room for these species we are also certain to lose the population of songbirds, wild flowers, butterflies and many other much-loved species which depend on the same habitats.

I very much hope that this book will help to show all those people – farmers, foresters, game-keepers, anglers, conservationists, people seeking recreation in the countryside, as well as planners, mineral extractors, water authorities and all other exploiters of the land – that their activities are not necessarily incompatible or mutually exclusive. In fact I am quite certain that, with goodwill and understanding, an harmonious balance can be achieved so that future generations will continue to be able to enjoy the same rich and varied natural heritage we know today.

Introduction

This book is a personal attempt to consider what I believe to be some of the most urgent and serious threats which face our game birds, mammals and fish. I have tried to discuss the problems and to show how the expert game biologist, the dedicated sportsman and the enlightened landowner can work together to avert these menacing influences and ensure a future for game and the many other species which share the same habitats.

I have treated all the principal gamebird species individually in separate chapters, concentrating on those aspects of their ecology which are of greatest importance in contemporary scientific research and the development of practical game management techniques. The brown hare is also discussed separately, but restrictions of space have made it impossible to deal with the mountain hare or the Irish hare. Deer and game fish, which can conveniently be grouped together into two distinct categories, are considered generically and not species by species, for reasons of space and also because many common factors apply to all of them.

This book is intended for the general reader, and so I have deliberately avoided scientific jargon, graphs, statistics and technical references which tend to interrupt the flow of the text and put up barriers between the reader and the story I have to tell. The technically minded can always consult the more specialist scientific publications, in which they will find the raw biological and ecological material which I have tried to condense here into a more readable and readily intelligible form for the layman.

Any discussion of game conservation is likely always to give rise to one particularly important and recurrent question. How does the sportsman reconcile his shooting, hunting or fishing, and the death of wild creatures which are inseparable from those activities, with any genuine concern for game species and their future well-being? Is there not a fundamental contradiction in the whole concept of conserving game?

I believe there is no such contradiction; and what follows has been written from a conviction that well-informed and intelligently regulated fieldsports play a vital part in ensuring a future not only for game but for their habitat which is also essential for the existence of countless other species of animals and plants. Any dispassionate assessment of the countryside of Britain and Ireland shows that our traditional fieldsports have been a major bastion against habitat loss and species decline. Without the sportsman's solicitude for his quarry and his efforts to maintain their habitat in the form of lakes and rivers, woodlands, hedgerows and upland moors, we would by now have lost much of the wildlife which we enjoy today.

Qui s'excuse, s'accuse. I do not believe that traditional fieldsports require any defensive apologia, from me or from anyone else. On the contrary, I feel that sportsmen have, perhaps characteristically, been far too reticent about showing how they have often been the most practical and effective of conservationists. For generations they have quietly got on with the vital business of managing and maintaining our populations of wild fish, game birds and deer, from which they have taken a carefully judged annual harvest or surplus. Their active stewardship of our heritage of game continues more vigorously and practically than ever, at a time when other sectors of the 'conservation industry' seem capable of little more than talking and abstract theorising.

No game species in these islands is threatened in any way by fieldsports as they are currently practised. Biologists and ecologists will testify to that. The threats to the future survival of game and all our wildlife lie elsewhere, and stem from pollution, from thoughtless and short-sighted forms of profiteering land use, and from all the growing pressures of man on the natural environment. Our traditional structures

1 *Red deer, pictured here on Exmoor, are indigenous to Britain and have been prized as game since the time of the Normans and their elaborate Forest Laws, from which today's Game Laws have evolved.*

of private land ownership and the carefully regulated exercise of privately controlled sporting rights over such land are among the most powerful and effective influences which will help to ensure that, as the twenty-first century approaches, there can still be a future for game and for our irreplaceable heritage of wildlife in general. The threats to game are serious and growing, but so too is the commitment and expertise of game biologists and sportsmen to ensure that game will survive.

'All hunting is a kind of love affair'. That was how Denys Finch-Hatton, that uniquely gifted Renaissance character of Africa in the 1930s – white hunter, poet, musician and classicist – explained his passion for game shooting to his friend, the authoress Karen Blixen. 'If you can hear a beautiful piece of music without wanting to learn it by heart; if you can see a beautiful woman without wishing to love her; if you can see a fine specimen of game without wishing to take it, you have no human heart'.

Heartless, too, are those who, through ignorance or indifference, might be prepared to allow our game to disappear. It must not be allowed to happen.

COLIN LAURIE McKELVIE
Broad Chalke,
Wiltshire
April 1985

Acknowledgements

I must first express my gratitude to His Royal Highness the Duke of Edinburgh for honouring this book with his Foreword. Prince Philip's active involvement with conservation organisations like the World Wildlife Fund and The Game Conservancy is well known, and in his Foreword he has identified the urgent challenges which must be faced if there is to be a future for game and other wildlife.

In the preparation of this book I received assistance and encouragement without which it might never have been completed. My colleagues at The Game Conservancy, especially my Director, Richard Van Oss, and the Director of Research, Dr Dick Potts and his scientific staff gave me invaluable guidance, especially on game biology. Much of the technical content of this book is attributable to their professional expertise, and to that of many other ecologists and biologists who have also helped me: errors and omissions are mine alone.

Richard Prior, author of the definitive *Trees and Deer* (1983) and professional consultant to the British Deer Society and The Game Conservancy, made some important contributions to my chapter on deer, as did Peter Keyser. Peter Lapsley, John Buckland and Crawford Little all provided stimulating ideas and information about game fish. A very special stimulus came from Jimmy Hamilton, Vice-President of Ireland's National Association of Regional Game Councils, to whom this book is dedicated. His infectious enthusiasm for the cause of game survival provided much of the motivation for my writing.

Merlin Unwin has been an unfailing source of advice and encouragement from the first commissioning of this book and at all stages of its production. Charles Jardine's line drawings have perfectly evoked the various game species and the environments they inhabit.

I must acknowledge the permission of the Editors of *Shooting Times and Country Magazine; Country Life; Sporting Gun* and *Countrysport* to incorporate some material which first appeared in their pages.

If my consideration of the issues in this book has an identifiable origin, it probably began almost thirty years ago when, as a very small boy, I came under the brief but lasting influence of two very remarkable men. Canon J. I. Lea was a gentle and kindly parson who had retired, after many years of missionary work in India, to fish his beloved Irish loughs. He was quick to identify an embryonic sportsman, took me fishing and gave me my first rod, and held me enthralled in his trophy-lined study, far past my six-year-old's bed-time, with stories of Indian tiger hunts and panther shoots.

John Craig is the wisest and most gifted schoolmaster I have ever known, either as a pupil or later when I was a member of that profession. Although not himself a sportsman, he saw in me the beginnings of a sporting bent and with typical understanding he knew how best to promote it. As my fourth form prep school prize he gave me N. M. Sedgewick's minor classic *The Young Shot*, and those gifts of a rod and a book did more than anything else to start me off on a sporting career and to lead me ultimately to a professional involvement in sport and conservation.

Finally, I am particularly grateful to my assistant, Judy Pittock, whose enthusiasm for the book was unflagging. Without the gallons of tea she made and the degree of orderliness which she tactfully and cheerfully imposed upon the manuscript and its author, my task would have been much harder.

Photographic acknowledgements

W. Beaumont 38, 40; T. H. Blank 3, 7, 9, 12, 30; R. Collins 20; D. Doble 1; Game Conservancy 2, 4, 14, 15, 26, 27, 31; G. S. Heddon 22; J. D.

Jackson 25; P. Lapsley 41; R. Lowes 19; C. L. McKelvie 16, 18, 23, 28, 29, 34, 35, 36, 39; R. Prior 33; M. W. R. Rands 5, 8, 10, 13; R. B. Robertson 21; J. Russell 6, 11; J. Tarlton 42; I. Thornber 42; D. Tutt 37; B. Walker 24; H. L. Watson and D. L. Lee 17.

1. Why 'Game'?

Why 'game'? How have we come to designate a comparatively small group of birds, mammals and fish by this term? Is it a valid category, and what makes these species different from other forms of wildlife?

The answers to all these questions have their roots deep in some of our oldest social, legal and recreational traditions and stem from man's prehistoric role as a hunter-gatherer. Fish, flesh and fowl comprise the chief sources of protein in our diet and what began ages ago as a straightforward quest for wildfowl, fish and large mammals as a source of food was later to become refined and formalised through ritualised hunting disciplines into the beginnings of what we know today as field sports. 'Game' in its generally accepted sense has come to denote those species which have always been particularly highly regarded for their culinary qualities, their aesthetically pleasing appearance and above all for the special thrill which accompanies their pursuit and capture. The hunting instinct is a concept familiar to anthropologists and psychologists, but their academic view is only a further acknowledgement of something very basic in Man – an atavistic impulse and aspiration which is still felt with undiminished excitement by everyone who wields a fishing rod or a sporting gun.

Game can have a narrower, more precise meaning, as defined for example by the 1831 Game Act, which is the legal basis of all modern British field sports but which, as amended by layer upon layer of subsequent legislation, is full of anomalies. The capercaillie, our largest and grandest woodland grouse, is clearly a game bird but is not actually classed as such by a law which was enacted at a time when it had become extinct as a British and Irish breeding species and had not yet been reintroduced from Scandinavia by British sportsmen. Snipe and woodcock are not game birds in the strict sense either, for their close season protection is a matter not for the Game Acts but for general wild bird protection laws, of which the Wildlife and Countryside Act 1981 is the most recent and most notable. When is a game bird not a game bird? When it is a snipe or a woodcock! Possession of a game licence is a legal requirement to take or kill snipe and woodcock, a prerequisite which does not apply to duck or geese. Game fish like the salmon, the sea trout and the brown trout have enjoyed a special sporting, culinary and economic status for centuries but the laws which govern the sporting fisherman in his pursuit of them are very different in England, Scotland and Ireland. Deer, too, are game in the eyes of some parts of the law and not others.

So we cannot look to the statute book for a clear-cut and generally accepted definition of what we mean by game. There are too many anomalies in these accretions of law which have built up by degrees over many centuries, and in our quest for a definition we find ourselves thrown back upon an unwritten consensus by which we *know* that the partridge, the sea trout and the roebuck are game while the teal, the grayling and the rabbit are decidedly not.

The tradition and practice of field sports is not concerned solely with game – the flighting woodpigeon and the bolting rabbit are as testing a quarry as any game shooter's target – but these sports continue to give a special status to those species which have enjoyed the highest sporting esteem in the British Isles for almost a thousand years. It was early monarchs such as King Canute and Malcolm II of Scotland who framed some of our first laws to protect deer and salmon, and the Norman conquest brought to Britain a formal structure of legislation which began with the Forest Laws of William I and was developed and elaborated by many of his successors.

The term 'game' seems first to occur in British law in an Act of 1389, in the reign of Richard II, and the word was linked directly with the defining of the property qualifications or social status necessary for anyone who wished to hunt or take 'gentlemen's game'. Property producing an income of forty shillings or more per annum was sufficient to entitle its owner to take game, while just over two hundred years later a form of sporting inflation had boosted the sum, for hunting deer, to an income of £10 per annum or a capital value of '£200 in goods'. However, if you happened to be the 'heir apparent of an Esquire' or 'the son of a Baron or Knight', or something higher on the social scale, your financial status was apparently irrelevant.

These feudal, hierarchical categories, so anachronistic to modern thinking, all stemmed from the fact that the king or queen laid claim to all game, and only those persons authorised by the sovereign might hunt it or take it by other means. The Forest Laws provided barbaric punishments by death, mutilation or blinding for those who presumed to take game above their station, and that tradition was to linger for a long time. Man-traps and spring guns were widely used

against poachers until they were finally banned early last
century, but the involvement of the Crown and the individual sportsman's ability to muster a small amount of cash
are still, in a residual form, part of our game laws in the 1980s.
The right to kill or take game is today conferred by the Crown
through a government department upon those who go to
their post office and buy a game licence, which now costs £6
per year. What began as a royal boon, the conferring of a
privilege upon the wealthy or the well-born, has become a
simple matter of a tax.

So much for the historical and legal aspects of game and the
ancient origins of those accumulated traditions and con-
ventions by which we have come to apply the term to some
species of mammals, birds and fish. Has the term any real
validity today? Is there any point in discussing these species
as a separate group? There are several good reasons for
answering yes to both questions.

Because game species have had such sporting importance
they have always attracted a great deal of study and attention
by generation after generation of sportsmen and countrymen. Species which are sought so eagerly with horse and
hound, dog and gun and rod and line have naturally
intrigued and fascinated sportsmen in a way which is
fundamentally different from other non-sporting species.
Human nature makes it inevitable that creatures which
supply sporting and gastronomic pleasure and also represent
an economic asset should invite a special degree of self-
interested and often very enlightened attention. The biology
of our game species has been as closely studied and is as
intimately understood as that of any other species, and much
more fully than most.

A historical example illustrates the ways in which enlightened self-interest can work and how it can change. Our
medieval forebears took a passionate interest in hawks and
falcons at a time when falconry or hawking was a pastime
open to everyone from the sporting parson and the yeoman to
kings and emperors. Before the development of fowling-
pieces and the art of 'shooting flying' a trained hawk or falcon

was the only means of catching a bird on the wing. Consequently falcons were highly prized, their natural history was closely studied and of great concern to the sportsman. But much of that unique understanding of raptors and their ways was lost or largely forgotten when game shooting later ousted the trained hunting hawk. Birds which had been treasured by sportsmen and princes soon became mere 'vermin', 'enemies of game' to be destroyed at every opportunity and their remains exhibited as grisly relics on the vermin gibbets of a vanished generation of gamekeepers in days gone by. As game providers the hawks and falcons had served their purpose, their day was over, and the sportsman and landowner of the eighteenth and nineteenth centuries turned his attention with zeal to a new style of 'game preserving'. The methods and techniques for taking game and the style and conduct of a day's sport have undergone a succession of radical revolutions over the centuries. Yet the sportsman-naturalist of the 1980s is participating in the long and unbroken tradition which looks upon game species with a particular and unique interest and affection.

If you shoot, or fish, or stalk deer or hunt the hare or the stag with hounds, you belong to a very ancient tradition. That is equally true of the trout fisherman casting his fly in a Highland burn, the game shooter swinging on to a high, curling pheasant rocketing out of a December woodland or the huntsman drawing for a hare with his pack of beagles or harriers. It all involves a particularly highly developed sense of dedication, enthusiasm and anticipation, together with elements of ritual, discipline and convention – and often a degree of financial expenditure too.

To think of game and other wildlife in terms of 'filthy lucre' brings us down to earth with jarring suddenness. But people are prepared to pay for the things they admire and desire, and when the demand for game shooting, game fishing and deerstalking exceeds the available supply, then the simplest of economic principles comes into effect. Today, anyone who can offer fishing, shooting or stalking of quality is in possession of a tangible, quantifiable economic asset. That fact plays a key part in the economics of the countryside of Britain and Ireland and those individual units, the privately owned farms and estates, of which it is composed, and also in the capital value of a woodland, a river or a heather moor. The deer and game birds in our woods, the salmon and trout in our fresh waters and the grouse on our heather uplands all confer wealth and richness – literal, aesthetic and spiritual – on the environments they occupy. The aesthetic pleasures of seeing a stag in a Highland corrie, or a salmon leaping up a waterfall, or a covey of partridges skimming across September stubbles are paralleled by the economic import- ance of these creatures as desirable quarry for the sportsman, and assets for the landowner.

Game of all types is a source of delight and also of down-to- earth income to sportsmen and landowners who are conser- vationists in the true sense of those who make wise use of a renewable natural resource. Flourishing game populations will yield a harvestable surplus each year – a crop which can be taken by the sportsman in pursuit of his traditional country recreations while leaving a sound breeding stock, the seed corn which ensures the future of the species and the sport it provides. If we lose our game, through pollution, loss of habitat or the unwise use of the countryside, we will have lost a source of sporting pleasure and of vital revenue to rural properties and the employment it generates, and an irreplaceable natural asset. The decline and eventual extinc- tion of our game species would be a disaster with repercus- sions for the well-being of our whole environment, for a landscape which sustains flourishing populations of game birds, mammals and fish will also support a rich diversity of other wildlife, including insects, songbirds, butterflies – yes, and predatory birds and mammals too.

The countryside of the British Isles and the wildlife which lives there depend ultimately upon the maintenance of the vital habitats without which most species will decline and disappear. The future of land and the many units, privately owned or state-controlled, of which it is composed lies firstly in the hands of the private landowners, the tenant farmers and the salaried managers of land owned by large institutions and the government. But it is a heritage which belongs, in a less direct but equally real sense, to us all. The pressure of general public opinion can and does influence the actions of particular groups and professions, and the post-war period has seen the rapid and continuing growth of a vigorous environmentally minded body of opinion in Britain and throughout the Western world. Concern for all our wildlife is growing, and environmental lobbying has become a political force to be reckoned with. The special place which game has traditionally occupied in our rural way of life has a crucially important role to play in this movement. The increasing depth and extent of our grasp of game biology makes game animals and fish particularly important as living barometers of the well-being of our environment in general.

Inevitably there are limits to how much traditional field sports can expand, and the sportsman-conservationist is aware that hunting, fishing and shooting could, if not carefully regulated, place excessive pressures on game and other species which are already hard pressed by pollution and many other factors. But here once again the enlightened self-interest of the sportsman intervenes to help secure the future of the species he loves. No one who enjoys his sport with rod, gun or rifle wishes to see the disappearance of the game species upon which that sport depends. Voluntary donations by sportsmen and from environmentally minded business and commercial organisations have made it possible for game biologists to learn more and more about our game species. Only if we have a thorough grasp of their biology and their basic needs in terms of habitat and food can we manage our game populations effectively in the future.

But the more we learn, the greater our awareness of the pressures which threaten the future survival of game in these crowded islands. With few exceptions, our game species are in general and country-wide decline. Yet this situation has given new impetus to our search for greater understanding of the 'private lives' of game species, so that effective management policies can be developed to secure a future for them into the next century.

In the chapters that follow I have tried to discuss some of the more important recent advances in our understanding of the biology of individual game species and groups of species, and to highlight some of the principal factors which threaten their survival. Each species deserves a book to itself and this general discussion can only try to focus on certain aspects of many very much wider subjects.

With species after species the message is clear: game is in decline. Yet the outlook is not entirely pessimistic. Our game biologists' knowledge and the practical expertise of game managers is growing all the time, and in many instances the answers to game survival have been discovered. We now know why we have lost such a large proportion of our grey partridges, and we have a blueprint which, if widely implemented, can reverse that decline and bring about a major recovery of partridge numbers. In many cases the expert know-how is readily available to ensure a future for game. But one crucial question remains to be answered – does there exist the *will* to implement the necessary management programmes and to secure a place for game in an integrated structure of multiple land use?

2. *The Pheasant*

Any realistic consideration of the game species of Britain and Ireland in the 1980s must give pride of place to the pheasant. Although it is not a native of these islands, there are many good reasons for according it this prominence. Pheasants are probably the game birds which spring most readily to mind when the average man hears the word 'game'. However dyed-in-the-wool a townsman he may be, the concept and probably the appearance of the pheasant will almost certainly be familiar. It is a bird which almost everyone, young or old, countryman or townee, could instantly identify at a glance. In addition to its obvious familiarity to the layman, the pheasant is overwhelmingly important for the British sportsman, since pheasants now account for a staggering 85 per cent or more of all the game shot in the British Isles.

The significance of pheasants in the national game bag entitles the species to supremacy as our most important single

2 *Familiar to everyone, pheasants are a common sight throughout the British Isles and now constitute over 85% of all game shot annually. They have been established here since the Middle Ages and wild populations are annually augmented by more than 10 million pheasants which are reared and released.*

game bird, in economic, sporting and social terms. It is now the staple sporting bird in these islands, a position which was formerly occupied by the indigenous grey partridge but is now firmly held by this much larger, more flamboyant and often decidedly exotic immigrant.

A mature cock pheasant is a magnificent bird, resplendent in all its gaudy iridescent plumage, but there is something flashy and just a little vulgar about the obtrusively exotic splendour of this bird which crows and struts among the dull duns and browns of our autumn and winter landscape. What a contrast it makes with the discreetly self-effacing appearance and demeanour of the little native partridge, now ousted from its former abundance as the commonest game bird of Britain's lowlands and farmland.

Although the pheasant is not indigenous to Britain it has

been with us in these islands for a very long time indeed. Successive generations of sportsmen and naturalists have firmly adhered to the belief that it was introduced by the Romans, but the evidence for this is actually rather slender. The ancient traditions maintain that Jason and the returning Argonauts were the first to bring the pheasant to Europe from its native haunts in the valley of the River Phasis in the Colchis region near the Caucasus, in what is now the Soviet Republic of Georgia. Ancient writers and naturalists like Pliny reiterated this, and the pheasant's formal taxonomic name – *Phasianus colchicus* – perpetuates it. We know from a variety of early sources that the pheasant was a table bird much favoured by the ancient Romans, who kept and reared them like domestic fowl, and who left detailed written accounts of their rearing methods and their cooking recipes. Since the pheasant was clearly a favourite dish there is every reason to suppose that the occupying Roman colonists brought them to Britain and that they may have been relatively common in the households and on the tables of the wealthier Romano-British. Thus our commonest game bird may well have begun its British career as a semi-tame farmyard fowl.

But any pheasants which found their way to Britain at that time were certainly not brought with sport in mind or with the intention that they should go feral and establish a self-sustaining wild population. Some may have escaped, but their role was intended to be that of semi-domestic fowl and nothing more. With the decline and fall of Roman influence the historical record becomes obscure and with it the subsequent fortunes of any feral populations of pheasants which may have survived in Dark Age Britain.

The status of the pheasant becomes a matter of more detailed record when we come forward more than seven centuries after the last Romans fled from Britain, past the great watershed of 1066 and into the Norman era. From the early twelfth century onwards the pheasant is regularly mentioned in documents of all sorts and it appears to have been regarded as an established wild bird in many parts of England. Reliable documentary evidence exists to show that wild pheasants were widespread and well established in many parts of Britain and Ireland by the fifteenth century. That early pheasant was what we would probably now refer to as the 'Old English' or 'black-necked' variety, lacking the prominent white collar of the ring-necked or Chinese pheasant *(Phasianus colchicus torquatus)*, and distinct also from the 'green' or melanistic form which is also common today. In fact the pheasants of our modern woods and fields are a thoroughly mongrel breed, a mixture of many forms in which the ring-neck is predominant but with wide variations ranging from the sombre dark greens of a melanistic pheasant to the very pale, almost white hens and, more rarely, cocks (known technically as flavistics) which occur quite regularly. Random cross-breeding in the wild has been compounded by the intensive rearing of countless millions of pheasants in game farms and hatcheries over the past century and a half, and the result has produced a gradient of plumage between the two extremes, and a thoroughly muddled variety of forms. It is important to distinguish these sporting varieties from the ornamental breeds like Golden, Silver, Japanese green and Lady Amherst pheasants, which, while they also belong to the pheasant family and will interbreed, are more properly to be regarded as collectors' birds, creatures of the aviary rather than of the fields and coverts. A glance at the contents of the game-cart on any modern pheasant shoot will reveal an enormous range and variety of coloration, but to the sportsman they are all simply pheasants.

On most shoots each season's bag will be made up of a 'harvest' of wild-bred birds, in addition to a proportion of reared and released pheasants. The scale on which pheasants are reared and released in Britain has been growing steadily over the past two centuries to a level which is currently estimated at more than 10 million birds each year. The size of this annual country-wide rearing and releasing operation clearly demonstrates the importance of the pheasant as our premier sporting species. Not only does it provide the bulk of game shooting on low-ground shoots; it is also responsible for generating a great deal of employment and income. The vast majority of gamekeepers in Britain and Ireland devote most of their time and energies to pheasant-related activities. Among low-ground keepers it is often the sole game species that they are directly concerned with, especially with the drastic decline in partridge numbers in recent decades. Without the pheasant there would be virtually no shooting and very few gamekeepers.

The great and growing demand for top-quality sporting pheasant shooting is such that a considerable minor industry has evolved to supply it. Natural wild-breeding populations of pheasants are continually augmented each summer by the careful release of millions of captive-bred poults, and on most low-ground shoots the bag will comprise both wild-bred pheasants and released stock. The ratio of wild to released is carefully monitored on many shoots, where reared birds are often marked before being released, usually by means of a coloured and numbered wing tag pinched into the fleshy part of the bird's wing joint called the patagium. This small and unobtrusive tag remains with the bird for the rest of its life and enables the gamekeeper or shoot organiser to identify shot birds and to segregate the bag into 'wild', 'released' and often 'released by someone else!' categories. If more shoot organisers can be persuaded to wing-tag their released birds and to report the results from an examination of each season's bag, these more complete data will be very helpful to game biologists.

As a general rule of thumb, an efficiently run pheasant shoot can expect to harvest about 40 per cent of its released birds during the season immediately following. Of the 60 per cent unaccounted for at the end of the season on 1 February a proportion will have fallen victims to predation, others will have succumbed to disease or death caused by accidental injury or severe weather, and some will simply have succeeded in eluding the guns.

There is an increasing amount of interest by shoot managers and game biologists in the eventual fate of the pheasants in this last category, those survivors which remain at large into the early months of each new year. On many of the larger, professionally organised shoots, the gamekeeper will carry out a well planned campaign of catching up, by which he will hope to live-trap sufficient hen and cock birds to form a captive breeding colony. This egg-producing unit will provide the eggs from which will be hatched the chicks destined for release into the coverts for the following season's shoots. Many gamekeepers will carry out this procedure as part of their annual routine, trapping a proportion of the February and March survivors in specially designed 'catchers' or live traps and placing cocks and hens together in a communal laying pen. Typically this will be securely enclosed with a high wire-netting fence and be designed so as to prevent access by foxes, feral cats, stoats and various other four-footed and winged predators. The eggs laid by laying-pen hens will either be removed for hatching in incubators or, less often today, placed under broody hens or bantams for hatching. This used to be a widespread practice but is now much less common and usually happens on the smaller type of shoot, which may well be run and keepered on a do-it-yourself basis by enthusiastic amateurs.

More often than not laying-pen eggs will find their way into modern, large-capacity incubators, either on the shoot or in a game farm. Some shoots will incubate, hatch and rear all their own pheasants from eggs laid in their own pens from caught-up birds from their own coverts. This 'self-sufficient' system is not universal and many shoots send their eggs to a game farm for incubation and hatching. A form of barter comes into operation here, with a shoot agreeing to supply the game farmer with a hundred eggs in exchange for perhaps forty day-old chicks, or a dozen six-week-old poults. In this way, and at a price, a shoot can delegate the responsibility for incubation and hatching to a professional game farmer, and need not undertake the hefty capital investment involved in the purchase of large-capacity incubators. If well reared poults are taken in return for eggs supplied, gas or electric brooders will not be necessary either, and poults at six or seven weeks of age will usually be ready for 'hardening off' in grassy pens before they go out to the final release pens in the coverts on the shoot.

The economics and cost-effectiveness of the various options available to shoot managers will vary depending on individual circumstances, and each year may involve some hardheaded rethinking and careful costing to decide the best and most appropriate strategy for a particular shoot. This is an important decision, and one which may well benefit from the services of a professional consultant in the person of the Game Conservancy's countrywide team of Game Advisors. If it is decided to send eggs to a game farm, it is only reasonable that the game farmer should expect to make a living, and he has a right to anticipate a fair return on his substantial investment in specialised incubating and rearing equipment. A full-time gamekeeper may perhaps be more economically employed if his incubating and rearing tasks are contracted out, leaving him time to get on with other chores and duties. But of one thing there can be no doubt whatever: reared pheasants are costly, and the costs are continually rising. An increasingly substantial outlay is now necessary to undertake an operation which in essence involves taking the pheasant's egg and nurturing it through the vulnerable and critical periods of incubation, hatching and the rearing of the young bird to release age.

It has been calculated by the Game Conservancy, based on a 1985 analysis, that it may cost between £10 and £12 to put a reared pheasant over the guns in November. The economics of pheasant releasing used to be vividly summed up in the phrase 'Up goes a guinea, bang goes tuppence, and down comes half-a-crown'. In 1985 costs are just a little higher! We can probably take £10 as the minimum cost of a reared pheasant, 10 pence as the price of a cartridge, and £1·75 as a good price for a shot bird sold off the game-cart to a dealer. You don't have to be a skilled accountant to see the built-in costs and losses in that financial structure.

In pleasing contrast to this, the wild-bred pheasant comes virtually free, requiring little more than the cost of leaving suitable nesting habitat, keeping predation under control, especially at nesting and fledging time, and providing winter food to hold birds on the shoot. For decades the main thrust

3 *A well balanced shooting programme will leave a healthy stock of pheasants to nest in the spring, but more research is needed to improve our knowledge of pheasant breeding biology. Like all ground-nesting game birds, incubating hen pheasants are vulnerable to predators like foxes. The newly hatched chicks benefit enormously from abundant insect food in their diet.*

of research and development work on pheasants has concentrated on the refining and streamlining of rearing and releasing techniques. This movement received its main impetus from the Victorian and Edwardian 'big shots', who demanded pheasants and lots of them for their epic battues, and the work was continued by later generations of sportsmen who very properly and responsibly sought to replenish and augment wild pheasant stocks by rearing and releasing as efficiently and economically as possible.

Today the trend in the shooting world is more progressive, towards high quality rather than mere quantity. More modest bags of high, fast-flying birds providing testing, sporting shots are increasingly in demand, and nothing can supply this top-quality sport better than truly wild pheasants. These are invariably tougher, faster and a more natural sporting proposition than even the best-conditioned reared birds. The presence of a flourishing population of wild-bred pheasants can also be taken as prima facie evidence of an environment rich in natural breeding habitat, suitable nesting cover and abundant insect and plant food for young chicks and adult birds. Such an environment does not only favour wild game but will probably also be rich in a wide variety of other wildlife, including songbirds, wild flowers and butterflies. This ideal can be achieved, and used to exist in many parts of Britain not so very long ago. On the light soils of Norfolk, for example, many estates used to achieve annual bags averaging more than one wild pheasant per acre, thanks to careful predator control, the maintenance of abundant nesting habitat, a diversity of crop types and a general absence of irresponsibly applied agrochemical sprays.

The radical innovations which have taken place in post-war farming methods have brought about many important and irreversible changes in Britain's lowland environment. Almost without exception these have militated against our wild game stocks, and in many cases against our general heritage of wildlife. And yet there are signs of an encouraging and growing trend away from the ruthless excesses of high-productivity prairie farming without regard for wildlife and the environment. Farmers have had a bad press in recent years and are becoming increasingly conscious of their responsibilities as the trustees and custodians of our country-side and its wildlife. The fortunes and future well-being of wild game is only one facet of a much wider issue, but it provides an important indicator of how our traditional lowland fauna and flora are faring.

Those released pheasants which survive the shooting season and escape the February catch-ups are often presumed either to fall victim to predators in the lean and hungry months of early spring or to join the wild breeding population. Sportsmen and game managers have always been confident that their rearing and releasing of pheasants has made a positive and substantial contribution to the size and breeding success of the wild stock. But is this in fact true? What proportion of surviving released hen pheasants actually succeed in hatching and rearing a brood of young in the spring after their release? As yet no one knows the precise answer, because the problem has never been studied properly. Like many aspects of wild game management in Britain, our knowledge of the reproductive success of these pheasants has been little more than what has been derived from generations of unsubstantiated opinion, haphazard observations and guesswork. Yet once again enlightened self-interest on the part of sportsmen is playing its part in moves to find out the answers. Sportsmen and landowners increasingly look to wild pheasants as a source of low-cost, high-quality sport and their need to know how best to promote flourishing wild pheasant populations has led to the setting up of the Game Conservancy's important 'Pheasants in the Wild' Research Project. A broadly similar parallel study is also being undertaken in the Republic of Ireland, funded by Ireland's National Association of Regional Game Councils.

This long-term study began by highlighting one very revealing and rather disturbing fact. Although the number of pheasants released annually in Britain has doubled between 1965 and 1985, the annual number of wild pheasants harvested has hardly increased at all. For the statistically minded, the annual national bag of wild pheasants has continued to fluctuate at around 45 birds per square kilometre. Why has a 100 per cent increase in the numbers of pheasants released not been followed by a much higher proportion of wild-bred pheasants? If only we knew more about the biology of wild pheasants it might have been possible to answer that question fairly readily, but our knowledge of the private life of the wild pheasant is abysmally slight and that is an indictment of earlier generations of sportsmen and game biologists. So much time, expense and effort has gone into the development of rearing and releasing techniques that the study of the basic biology of wild pheasants has been almost totally neglected.

The Game Conservancy's team of biologists have set themselves the task of responding to the demands of sportsmen, conservationists and landowners by finding out more about the natural history of wild pheasants. If research can identify the essential requirements of wild-breeding pheasants and develop practical management techniques to satisfy those needs the consequences for wild pheasant stocks, sport and wildlife in general may be very far-reaching. Success in this venture will mean thriving, self-sustaining pheasant populations which can be harvested intelligently so as to provide top quality sport, the continued employment of gamekeepers and many benefits to others involved in the wider economic sphere of field sports. Traditional habitat will be preserved and extended, benefiting a whole range of wildlife, and pheasant shooting will be an even more genuine field sport – in the true sense of the sporting pursuit of wild game in its natural environment.

The current situation of our wild-breeding pheasant population and the failure of a greatly increased number of released birds to boost it significantly must be seen in the general context of the countryside and the changes which have been taking place in it over recent years. There has been an agricultural revolution on a massive scale in post-war Britain and Ireland and its effects have had a major impact on almost every form of farming and land use in these islands. Increased mechanisation has made farming much less labour-intensive than it traditionally was, and diesel-engined machinery has swept away the 'horse-hoeing husbandry' as promoted by eighteenth century agricultural innovators like Jethro Tull. New methods have been developed in a ceaseless quest for increased efficiency, higher productivity and more profit. Farming, forestry and other forms of rural land use have always been evolving and changing, and will presumably continue to do so. Britain's wild game has had to contend with a succession of major agricultural and social changes. When medieval man developed strip-farming, that too must have constituted a big environmental upheaval for lowland wildlife, although there were no game biologists around then to record it. The technological innovations and new agronomic regimes of the 1970s and 1980s are only the most recent manifestations of a long and continuing process.

Since, as the statistics clearly show, reared pheasants have failed to increase the wild population, the reason for this failure must be sought by studying the bird's habits and biological needs. It seems evident that something has gone wrong, some factor or combination of factors is preventing the post-shooting 'February survivor' from breeding effectively and making a significant contribution to the wild pheasant population.

The 'Pheasants in the Wild' Research Project is undertaking an intensive study of wild pheasants on mixed farmland on a study area in Hampshire. It is a landscape typical of much of lowland Britain and of the sort of areas in which most pheasant shoots take place. The study of the pheasants ranges from straightforward visual observation and counting of birds to the most sophisticated modern radio-tracking techniques. Pheasant research, like so many other aspects of the study of animal behaviour, has been revolutionised by the development of miniaturised radio transmitters. Tiny radios, weighing only a few grams and powered either by minute batteries or by solar energy, can be fitted to a wide range of creatures. Once 'bugged' in this way each individual can be tracked and its activities monitored around the clock for weeks or even months on end, until the animal's death or an electronic failure in the equipment puts an end to the stream of informative transmissions.

Pheasants, both cocks and hens, have been radio-tagged and their subsequent movements and activities closely followed. Gradually an increasingly clear picture has emerged of how the cock birds display, establish territories and acquire harems of females with which to mate. By early spring the cock birds will each have identified a territory of about five acres on average, and will have begun to 'beat the bounds' of their chosen areas, advertising their presence by

4 *Radio-telemetry – here applied to a cock pheasant – is a major aid to biologists in studying the private lives of birds and mammals. The movements and activities of a number of radio-tagged individuals can be monitored continually over several months.*

crowing and displays of noisy wing-flapping or 'drumming'. Unlike the high, bleating vibrato of a drumming snipe, the wing-drumming sound of a pheasant is a resonant and powerful explosive noise. The crowing call, which is not unlike that of the familiar domestic rooster, a distant relative, is both an appeal and a challenge. It serves to assert the cock's dominance over his territory and to intimidate would-be rivals and intruding cocks, while alerting the sexually receptive hen birds in his harem to his presence. It may also be imitative or triggered off by the stimulus of other vibrations. My evening roe stalking among the woodlands of Dorset is often punctuated by outbursts of crowing from cock pheasants in response to the sonic boom as Concorde crosses the south coast.

Crowing and wing-drumming are signs of the aggressive bravado characteristic of many male game birds in the breeding season. It is often performed in some prominent place where the cock pheasant can see and, more important, be seen. A bank, wall or any conveniently conspicuous place may be used, and the bird's motivation is identical to that of the farmyard cockerel, which traditionally chooses the top of the dunghill from which to proclaim his presence with noisy defiance.

A confrontation with another male will result in displays and posturings which are also similar to those of the domestic fowl. Neighbouring cocks may meet on their respective territorial boundaries and vigorous crowing, strutting and head-tossing will ensue. The red wattles will be engorged and prominent and may be the first target of beaks and claws if the encounter should come to blows. This often happens, but such events are rarely prolonged and almost never fatal. Noise, bluster and aggressive display are more important than actual physical violence in establishing the eventual dominance of the stronger bird, and the defeated opponent will usually retreat quite promptly, scuttling off in a crouching posture which proclaims his admission of defeat.

The pheasant's crowing calls are familiar to anyone with even the slightest knowledge of the countryside – the crowing of cock birds going up to roost at dusk, the clattering alarm call of a bird flushed by a potential predator or by beaters on a shooting day, and the crowing call of the displaying cock pheasant in spring. But the vocal repertoire is not limited to these louder and more obvious sounds. A clucking sound not unlike that of a contented farmyard fowl often indicates that a pheasant feels anything but contented or secure. A distinct wariness and agitation can lead to this 'kok-ok, kok-ok' call, which may be a preliminary to a hasty dash for cover or a rapid escape flight. There is also a range of other gentler, low-key calls, including those in the hen bird's vocabulary. As befits her role in the scheme of things at breeding time, the female's calls are designed not to advertise her presence, which would be an unwise invitation to predators intent upon the destruction of her, her eggs or young. So long as she knows the whereabouts of the cock bird, as announced by his crowing, contact and mating can proceed. Some of her most important calls are used to bring together her young chicks and to alert them when danger threatens.

The breeding hen will choose her nesting site and will become part of a harem of females which may number as many as seven or eight individuals. Usually a cock's territory will encompass a range of habitat types, and these may include hedges, woodland, arable crops, open pastureland and untended weedy corners with low shrubs, brambles and rough grasses.

The density of territory-holding cock pheasants is related to the availability of woodland and field-edge habitat. Males adopt an unusual mating system, known technically as 'harem defence polygyny', in which the cock defends the females in his harem from sexual attacks by other males and also keeps a lookout for predators while the hen birds are feeding. This is made possible by the nature of the pheasant's digestive system, which permits the intake and digestion of food only at a certain rate. This forces the males to rest periodically from feeding and they can then adopt this defensive role towards their harem of hens. Perhaps since the most vigilant and effectively defensive males allow their hens to feed more securely, they are more successful in attracting and holding larger harems.

Hen pheasants will not nest within the cock bird's territory, and after mating the harem of feeding hens may wander across the territories of several males, for the feeding range of hen harems is much larger than individual male territories. Hen pheasants will often nest somewhere near the edge of their feeding range, and this may help to minimise density-related losses due to predation. Although pheasants make extensive use of woodland in late autumn and winter, usually venturing into the open only to feed, there is much more activity in open fields in springtime. This leaves the exposed birds visible to predators but the harem defence strategy largely offsets this.

As a ground-nesting species, the pheasant fares best when nests enjoy protection from the wind and rain, concealment from the sharp eyes of potential predators, and good drainage to reduce the risk of inundation following spring cloud-bursts. Security from predation during the incubation period is important if nesting is to result in high chick productivity. If a fox or feral cat kills a sitting hen that nesting attempt is obviously a total write-off. Not only has the hen been lost but so too have any chicks that she might eventually have reared. Less catastrophic but still serious are heavy losses of eggs and young chicks. Eggs may be taken by a wide range of predators, with foxes, feral cats, stoats, weasels and feral mink all representing potential threats, and to these mammal predators we must add carrion and hoodie crows and other corvid species.

The ways in which these various predators go about their hunting, their predatory tactics and their effects upon the nesting success of game birds are not fully understood, and more research on predation will result in a much fuller understanding of how predators affect the abundance or scarcity of their prey. From this knowledge it should be possible to develop techniques of predator control which will be effective in promoting optimum breeding productivity and chick survival among game, while avoiding the excesses of former generations, when game preservation was synonymous with the thoughtless and unceasing destruction of many non-game species.

The hen pheasant will lay a clutch of pale, olive-green, uniformly coloured eggs which may vary in number from nine to fifteen. Incubation begins as soon as the clutch is complete. Incubation of the eggs and care of the young brood are the responsibility of the hen alone; the incubation period averages 23–28 days. Like the young of many game birds, pheasant chicks are active and mobile within hours of hatching – 'precocial' in the language of biologists. Like partridge and grouse chicks, newly hatched pheasants follow the hen bird as she moves in and around the family's home range. At this point a number of critical habitat-related factors will combine to influence the survival of the chicks. Suitable habitat will ensure shelter from the elements, refuge from predators and ample food of the right type for the chicks.

The diet of adult pheasants is known to include a wide range of cereal grains, weed seeds, berries and similar items, but we have hitherto known very little about the food requirements of young chicks, and the relative importance of certain types of food for their growth and survival. With partridges, decades of research have shown conclusively that the chicks must have insects to eat if they are to survive, though the red-legged partridge is rather less insect-dependent than the grey partridge. Not only is the survival rate of grey partridge chicks much higher in areas where insects abound; a quite staggering 91 per cent of that survival rate is attributable to insects alone. But what of insects and pheasant chicks? How important are insects in their diet and in promoting their survival through the perilous days after hatching?

Radio-tracking was the first step towards answering this question. By 'triangulating' – getting two or more directional fixes – on a radio-tagged hen and her brood at their overnight roosting site, usually in the middle of a field of growing cereals, scientists could find the roost and collect the chicks' droppings for microscopic analysis. When these rather dry excretions are preserved in alcohol and later dissolved in water, they can be viewed under a microscope at a magnification of about 120×. This reveals the presence of certain undigested pieces of food and debris. These can be identified and counted and will show what the chicks have been eating. The survival rate of various broods of pheasant chicks can be compared with their respective diets and the areas over which they have ranged with the hen bird in search of food. The results of these studies since 1983 have been very revealing and point to insects as a crucially important factor in pheasant chick survival.

5 *A directional aerial gives the game biologist a 'fix' on one of his radio-tagged birds. Two or more fixes will enable him to pinpoint its position. Here the aim is to locate the overnight roost site of a hen pheasant with her brood of chicks. Their droppings, collected and analysed, give important clues to their diet and how it affects chick survival.*

Three of the main insect food items taken by pheasant chicks on the Hampshire study area are caterpillars, carabid beetles and Heteroptera (plant bugs). Parts of the anatomies of these creatures cannot be digested by the chicks and show up when the droppings are analysed. The mouth pieces or mandibles of caterpillars and carabids tend to remain identifiable, as do the hard egg-laying tubes or ovipositors of plant bugs.

Two broods of wild pheasant chicks were carefully monitored in 1983 and their survival rate was compared with their intake of insect food and the areas over which they ranged while feeding. The results give some important pointers for the future management of wild pheasant populations.

Brood A had a large home range and wandered far and wide, but most of its activity was in a large field of winter

wheat. Insect availability in the area was poor, chiefly owing
to the insecticidal effects of agrochemical sprays. Three
weeks after hatching only 18 per cent of the chicks were still
alive. A very different and much happier fate awaited the
chicks in brood B, which occupied a much smaller area where
two fields converged. Maize and winter wheat grew side by
side and adjoined a patch of fat-hen weed – aptly named in
view of its value to gallinaceous birds. This area contained
over 200 times the density of insect food items of the much
larger home range of the ill-fated brood A, and 56 per cent of
brood B survived to the age of three weeks – more than three
times better than the others. The larvae of sawflies, lepidop-
tera and heteroptera occurred more frequently in the droppings of brood B, while carabid beetles formed a larger
proportion of the diet of the less successful brood. This family
had also to feed over a large area of its wheatfield home range
to find enough beetles, which were not abundant in the crop.
Brood B, with its much higher survival rate, was found to
have eaten fourteen times more caterpillars than brood A,
and heteroptera were absent from the diet of the less successful chicks. Further work during the following year on eight
more broods supported these early results.

From this case history of two pheasant broods it was seen
that a diversity of vegetation and crop types within a
comparatively small area and an abundance of these three
main insect groups contribute greatly to the survival of the
young chicks, in this instance trebling the rate of survival.
But game biologists are professionally cautious people and
reluctant to jump to conclusions based on small study
samples and short periods of research. Time will tell us a great
deal more about the insect factor, and we need to know more
too about the effects of predation and how they can best be
minimised. And game research, however fascinating its
conclusions, is of practical value to the sportsman, landowner
or environmentalist only if we can find ways of turning our
knowledge into practical game management techniques.
Game is only one element among many in the total pattern of
land use in the British Isles today. Ways must be found in

which agriculture, forestry and the many new and growing forms of recreational use of the countryside can be reconciled to give a harmoniously integrated countryside.

If, as seems likely, insects are as vital for wild pheasants as for wild partridges, it is both pointless and unhelpful to turn to the arable farmers and say bluntly, 'Thou shalt not spray'. High productivity and efficient modern arable farming depend heavily upon the use of agrochemicals, and it would be naive in the extreme to expect their use to be abandoned in favour of bigger populations of game birds. The challenge for game biologists and progressive farmers is subtler and more complex. It involves the development of a carefully devised and thoroughly tested strategy for sustaining high arable crop yields side by side with flourishing populations of wild game. Many topics will have to be considered, and these will include the optimum size of fields, the maintenance of hedges of the best type for ground-nesting game birds, and the informed and judicious use of agrochemicals so as to give maximum benefit to crops while doing minimum damage to the insect life which we now know is essential to wild game bird chicks.

The development of such a strategy, which will be widely acceptable to farmers, is the aim of an important new research and development project, devised and funded by farmers who are concerned not only about their crop yields but also about the effects of agrochemicals on farming and wildlife in general. This has been an encouraging development at a time when farmers have been heavily criticised in many quarters for failing to work the land responsibly so as to preserve its ecology and safeguard our heritage of wildlife. This Cereals and Gamebirds Project is discussed later in more detail in connection with the grey partridge, but its findings are already showing some exciting new signs of how modified spraying can greatly benefit wild pheasant numbers. Pheasant broods were found to be much larger – sometimes three times as large – on areas where weedy field edges or headlands had been left unsprayed, compared with broods on cereal fields which had been conventionally sprayed right up to the hedges or fences.

Later, in the chapters on partridges, there is a discussion on the recently developed 'management blueprint' for these species. Its approach to the problem rests upon the assumption that there are three principal prerequisites if the game bird population is to flourish. There must be adequate habitat for feeding, shelter and refuge from predators; adequate supplies of the food items required by the birds at their different periods of development; and an acceptable level of predation which does not put the game bird population under excessive pressure. The supreme importance of the pheasant as our most numerically significant game bird makes it an urgent priority to develop a proven, practical and readily implemented management blueprint to promote wild pheasant numbers. It seems likely that pheasants and partridges will both benefit from a common strategy. Most important, these benefits will not be confined to game shooting alone, for an environment which promotes flourishing game bird stocks will be rich in wild flowers, insects, other birds and mammals too. A recurrent theme in modern game management is that what is good for game tends to be good for wildlife in general.

3. *The Grey Partridge*

When the redoubtable Colonel Peter Hawker set out on 1 September 1827 to enjoy the first day of the partridge shooting season, at Longparish in the valley of the Test in Hampshire, he expected a good bag of wild grey partridges (*Perdix perdix*). In fact he came home with 51 brace of them to his own flintlock gun – an astonishing day's partridge shooting for a solitary gun, especially in those days of comparatively primitive fowling pieces and at a time when 'shooting flying' had only recently become practicable and socially acceptable in Britain. Most remarkable of all, to anyone taking stock of our grey partridge populations a century and a half later, is the abundance of birds which must have been available to enable Hawker to make such a bag. Sadly, it is all very different today, even in once-classic partridge counties like Hampshire.

Hawker pursued his fanatically dedicated shooting career in a landscape very different from that which we know today. Smaller fields divided by thick, grassy-bottomed hedges, often maintained on a regular cut-and-lay system, made for a mosaic of diverse arable crops and grassy meadows, where the hay was cut and the corn reaped by hand, leaving long stubbles which usually lay all winter until spring ploughing time. Partridges were the commonest game birds throughout lowland Britain and Ireland, indigenous to these islands and eastwards across continental Europe. In medieval times they were a popular delicacy – Chaucer's gourmandising Franklin kept caged partridges to supply his elaborate table – and the native 'common partridge' was the staple game bird for the falconer, the netsman with his 'setting spaniels' and the shooter with his pointing dog and flintlock 'birding piece'.

Queen Victoria had been on the throne for thirty years before shooting over pointing dogs or walking up gave way to driven or battue shooting as the general pattern on partridge shoots. A modified form of the Continental practice of partridge driving began in England in the 1850s and by the 1880s some of the classic partridge manors were producing their daily bags of a thousand birds or more. Distasteful though it is for the modern sportsman-conservationist to rehearse these statistics of the excessive bags of earlier generations, it reveals a great deal about the contemporary abundance of a game bird which far outweighed the pheasant in numbers and sporting importance. In the 1980s the pheasant has assumed an overwhelmingly dominant position over all other game birds and few British game shots will now get more than an occasional chance of a shot at a wild grey partridge in the course of a whole season. In many parts of Ireland, Wales and Scotland he may be lucky even to see one for seasons on end.

The story of the grey partridge and its twentieth-century decline is one of the saddest tales in the history of our game species. It is made all the more poignant by the fact that we know a great deal about how and why it happened, we have a good grasp of the practical measures which might bring about its recovery, and yet we see the total British Isles population in continuing decline.

Despite the shift of emphasis brought about by the 'big

6 *The grey partridge is an established game bird of farmland across the British Isles and Northern Europe, but is now much less common than formerly. Once the principal game bird of the lowground sportsman in Britain and Ireland, it has now declined seriously in most areas, principally because of habitat loss, agrochemical spraying and predation pressure.*

shots' of late Victorian and Edwardian days who wanted their large bags of driven pheasants, the grey partridge was the premier sporting bird in Britain and Ireland up to the outbreak of the First World War. Gamekeepers, many of whom went off to the war, were never replaced in the same numbers, the carefully managed partridge manors had begun to decay and by the early 1920s the country-wide ascendancy of the pheasant was well under way. At that time Eley, the ammunition manufacturers, had a near-monopoly of the British and Irish market in sporting cartridges and they saw their sales, and thus their profits, falling as the partridge population declined. The majority of cartridges used on low-ground shoots had always been fired at partridges. The scarcity of the partridge was reflected by reduced ammunition sales and it was a logical step for Eley to set up a research unit to investigate the decline, try to identify its causes and develop practical ways of arresting and reversing the trend. This self-interested but enlightened measure led to the setting up of a game research unit which was later to become the Eley Game Advisory Service and ultimately the Game Conservancy, an independent voluntary body since 1970 and now a registered charity. It is the only organisation in the British Isles wholly devoted to scientific research into game species and the development of practical game management techniques based on a firm foundation of biological under-standing. This is in contrast to many other countries, where game biology and management enjoy major support from public funds. The Game Conservancy relies almost entirely upon voluntary subscriptions and sponsorship to support its work, and the enlightened self-interest of a cartridge manu-facturer has now been replaced by that of the enlightened sporting community. Partridge biology remains in the front line of their research work, as it has for over half a century. This has resulted in a vast amount of accumulated data on partridges in Britain and a uniquely comprehensive under-standing of the species. So why has the partridge declined and, in the light of all this study, why have landowners and game managers failed to increase its wild populations?

The grey partridge and the story of its decline really deserves a book to itself, and will shortly have one, but it is possible to summarise the principal factors which have played a part in it – habitat, predation and food.

The partridge's year begins in late autumn and early winter, when the birds live in coveys or family parties, which generally consist of two or more old birds and their various young. In a really good year there may be a high young to old ratio with seven or eight juveniles with their parents. In poor years the ratio may be one to one. At this stage in their year, partridge populations will probably include rather more males than females, because about a quarter of the adult breeding hens are killed each year during the incubation period, often predated on the nest by a fox or perhaps a feral cat or a stoat. Mink too can be a problem in many areas.

These coveys are typical of what the sportsman sees during the shooting season and they tend to lie very tight until the whole covey flushes at the close approach of a man or a dog. A covey lying out on a grassy field or on stubble can be very conspicuous as they move about and feed with their heads up. A hint of danger will make them squat, sinking down to take maximum advantage of the available cover and remaining thus until either the danger has passed or the dogs or beaters have come close enough to flush them. They rise with a blur of wings and a slightly grating, gravelly call, and the explosive flush of the covey is an important defensive technique. Any predator is likely to be disoriented by a sudden burst of small brown shapes – not least the sportsman, who needs to take a steady shot at one bird and resist the temptation to 'fire into the brown'. Their flight is not as fast as the blur of fast-beating little wings makes it appear. In fact partridges fly much more slowly than pheasants or grouse, but their bomb-burst flushes, their relative agility on the wing and their deceptive pace make them a very testing quarry, especially when they are driven over hedges to standing guns in the classic manner.

They do not generally fly very far and grey partridges are amongst the most sedentary of birds; they may spend their whole lives in just three or four adjacent fields. Generations of sporting writers have recounted with obvious affection the settled domesticity of the partridge with its unobtrusive, monogamous way of life among the hedgerows and arable fields of lowland Britain. Yet that is a landscape which has undergone a rapid and fundamental transformation this century, and especially in the post-war period.

The coveys begin to break up in mid-winter as the birds pair off, though this may be delayed in severe winters, when the coveys may remain together until as late as February or early March. The old cocks and young hens which cannot find mates within the covey disperse to pair up with others, to be followed later by the unmated young cock birds. In normal years this pairing and spring dispersal will be complete by late February. In the bare landscape of the countryside at that time of year the birds are easy to spot and a complete census of the partridge population on an area may be possible if spring counts are carried out thoroughly. An observer with binoculars working from a vehicle in calm, dry conditions and concentrating his efforts at dawn and dusk can identify and count the pairs with much greater accuracy than is possible if one goes around an area on foot.

Paired partridges will be able to nest and rear their broods successfully only where there is suitable nesting habitat. As a ground-nesting bird which needs to conceal its nest from the eyes of predators, the partridge favours hedgerows with a good growth of grasses and other cover in the bottom. A raised, well drained hedge bank will keep the nest site dry and protect the eggs and chicks from the risk of inundation by summer thunderstorms and cloudbursts, which can cause heavy local mortality in a matter of minutes. Hedges should be dense and 'Π'-shaped in section, from 3 to 6 feet thick and not so high as to inhibit hedge-bottom growth by excessive shading.

But there is no point in even discussing the optimum shape and design of hedges if they have been grubbed out and removed completely. Yet this is the case in many parts of the country where once the partridge flourished but where it is

7 *The hen partridge prefers to nest in grassy, well-drained hedge bottoms and sits so tightly that you can stroke an incubating hen. If she leaves her eggs she will cover them up, but the sitting hen is particularly vulnerable to predatory mammals. Much partridge nesting habitat has been lost because of hedgerow removal.*

now severely depleted, sometimes to vanishing point. Arable farming and in particular the growing of cereals are closely linked to the distribution of the partridge, and this type of farming has become much more intensified and mechanised in recent decades. The trend has been towards larger fields, created by the amalgamation of several smaller ones by the removal of the hedges, and so we have arrived at the 'prairie farming' landscape now typical of large areas of our cereal-growing counties. Loss of hedgerow nesting habitat either forces the birds to adopt the much less satisfactory alternative of nesting in the cereal crop itself or causes them to move elsewhere. In either case the removal of hedges to create very large fields results in a much lower density of nesting pairs and consequently a very reduced harvestable surplus for the sportsman.

Game biologists have concluded that the optimum amount of hedgerow for partridges on light-soiled arable land is 19 miles per thousand acres, which is easier to grasp if we think in terms of an average field size of 25 acres. To the modern intensive arable farmer that is too small for his high-yield targets, and hedges have been removed in order to enable machinery to manoeuvre more easily, to minimise the shading effect of hedges on the growing corn and to eliminate the likelihood of the invasion of the crop by weeds and certain injurious species of insects which may be harboured by hedges. Relatively small arable fields were familiar to Colonel Hawker and were manageable in the days of hand reaping, before the development of large machinery and agrochemical crop sprays. Those were the days of real partridge abundance. The trend towards a well manicured landscape of large weed- and insect-free cornfields has been very damaging to partridges and thus to the sport they can provide. The loss of nesting habitat has had serious effects but to that must be added the further problems of reduced food availability and the increased pressures of predation.

We know that young partridge chicks must have insects in their diet if they are to survive. This is absolutely fundamental to the growth and development of the newly hatched chick and has been repeatedly confirmed by years of research by the Game Conservancy's scientists. Certain species of insects are especially important and these include sawfly larvae, plant bugs, weevils, leaf beetles and diurnal ground beetles. It has been known for some time that these protein-rich foods are essential if the young chick is to flourish. Its digestive system is simply not adapted to cope with a diet of weeds and grain seeds and other fibrous cellulose foods which the adult partridge can grind down and digest with the help of its gizzard. Vegetable food is not only much less digestible by the chick but also represents a much poorer source of the protein-rich nutrients which the growing bird needs. This need for insect food is now known to be shared by the pheasant, the red grouse and the black grouse, as recent research has revealed, and this is discussed elsewhere in connection with these other species.

Arable farming, and cereal growing in particular, is ill disposed towards insects. Some, such as aphids, can do serious damage to growing crops and a major aphid outbreak is something the farmer dreads. But aphids have their natural enemies and there are other insect species – technically known as polyphagous predators – which feed on aphids and often help to keep their numbers in check, so preventing a major aphid outbreak. But the farmer cannot always rely upon such natural controls and the development of insecticides has been inevitable. Sprays which kill all insects indiscriminately are now widely used and, like the rain, they fall on the just and on the unjust. Aphids and other damaging species are destroyed, but so too are their natural predators and all the species of insects which partridge chicks must have to eat if they are not to die within a day or two of hatching.

Insecticidal action is found not only in those agrochemicals which are specifically intended to kill insects. It can also be an incidental effect of some herbicide and fungicide sprays. Herbicides (weedkillers) are used by the farmer to destroy the weeds and other vegetation which may otherwise invade and contaminate the cereal crop. Fungicides are designed to counteract fungal diseases which can attack growing crops. Crops which are 'dirty' with weeds and attacked by fungal growths are inevitably less profitable for the farmer and less acceptable to the purchaser of the harvested grain. A tidy farm and a high-yield, clean crop, undamaged by insects or disease, have been the twin aims of post-war arable farming.

Partridges, however, have not responded well to this agricultural revolution. Apart from the scarcity of good nesting hedges in many areas, the direct and indirect effects of many agrochemicals and the ways in which they are used have deprived those remaining partridges of the vital insect diet for chicks. If the insects' host plants – such as pheasant eye, corn gromwell and fat-hen – are killed by sprays there is

8 *Radio tagging has been a vital aid to the study of grey partridge breeding success. The movements of food and hens and their broods can be closely studied, and insects are continually demonstrated to be vital in the young chicks' diet. Can agrochemical spraying techniques be modified to improve partridge survival, while maintaining cereal yields?*

little or no insect food for the newly hatched chicks. If sprays drift on the wind into the bottoms of hedges it may mean that the chicks will hatch out into a hostile and sterile environment, lacking the cover of weeds and grasses to conceal them from predators and devoid of that vital protein source in the form of plant bugs, beetles and other insects.

Nesting habitat and insect food represent two vital contributions to partridge abundance – bed and board for the breeding adults and their chicks. The third component in this three-cornered relationship is predation and its effects upon nesting and newly hatched partridges. These three factors are seen as vitally interdependent in the 'blueprint for partridges' which is the outcome of decades of study by biologists of the Game Conservancy and others. A useful analogy is a three-legged stool. Which 'leg' or factor is the most important in sustaining the whole structure? In fact, to weaken or remove any one of them is to destabilise the total structure and to risk its collapse.

The partridge is unusually vulnerable to predation, especially by mammals such as foxes and stoats. A hen partridge is a diligent mother, sitting tight on her eggs even when the gravest danger threatens. You can sometimes bend down and stroke a hen partridge as she sits on her nest, and this shows how easy it is for a predator to kill the sitting hen if it is located. The loss of an incubating female is a major disaster, of course. It means the loss not only of an adult bird but also of the brood which she would otherwise have hatched and reared, and such an event is quite literally a dead loss to the partridge population. Yet such predation tends to run at a high level during the nesting period and the most recent data show that these losses can amount to some 4 per cent *per day* during the critical incubation period. Where partridges are abundant and there is ample nesting cover the effects of nest predation become even greater, and a field size of approximately 25 acres is generally regarded as a good midway point between the extremes of prairie-farm hedge-row scarcity and an excess of nesting habitat which encourages heavy density-related predation.

The carrion crow and other corvids will take partridge eggs and for this reason the hen bird always covers up her nest when she leaves it, unless some extreme disturbance pushes her suddenly off the eggs and she flees without covering them. The promotion of a dense grassy growth in the bottoms of hedges and in rough untidy corners enables partridges to site their nests in places where there is good natural cover, but this is where extreme agricultural tidiness and the effects of herbicide sprays will make the nesting bird and its eggs even more vulnerable.

Predators, whether mammals or corvids, are only a real threat to partridges and other game birds at nesting time. Traditional partridge keeping involved the annual implementation of rigorous predator control to ensure that the principal predatory species were reduced to acceptably low levels in spring, to minimise predation losses. The old-style partridge keeper spent a great deal of his time trapping, snaring and shooting predators and providing the nesting birds with as secure an environment as possible in which to nest and raise their young. Today's gamekeeper, however, usually has very different priorities and works in a very different way from the partridge keeper of a generation or two ago.

Economic, agricultural and social changes have all played a part in this. The British gamekeepering tradition was at its peak before the outbreak of the First World War, with an estimated 25,000 full-time gamekeepers in Britain and Ireland. But labour was relatively much cheaper in late Victorian and Edwardian times and a comparatively modest partridge manor of perhaps 1,500 acres probably maintained a head keeper and three beatkeepers, none of whom had any pheasant-rearing duties or other general estate work to conflict with their principal tasks of controlling the predators and managing the habitat. In the 1980s a full-time game-keeper will probably have to cope single-handed with upwards of a thousand acres, tackling all the many seasonal tasks with whatever occasional assistance he can find, and usually undertaking a major pheasant rearing and releasing programme. This involves several hours daily around the rearing field and the release pens at a critical time of the year for partridges when his predecessor of seventy years ago would have been concentrating his efforts on predator control.

The old-style keeper walked or bicycled around his beat and knew it with an intimacy which is simply impossible for the modern game manager, heavily committed to pheasant rearing and other tasks in addition to doing his rounds by Land Rover. To maintain an effective line of traps and snares, each of which must by law be inspected daily, and preferably twice each day, was much easier when a beat of three or four hundred acres was patrolled regularly on foot, and a large number of traps could be operated right across the shoot. Today any single-handed gamekeeper will do well to oversee more than eighty or a hundred traps on a thousand-acre shoot, committed as he is to a wide range of other jobs.

The virtual disappearance of the old regimes of rigorous spring predator-control has been the third progressively weakened leg of the partridge's supporting structure, and these three factors have conspired to bring about a relentless downward spiral. The statistics are eloquent: only 5 pairs per square kilometre in the once-productive arable parts of the eastern counties of England which used to have densities of up to 80 pairs in the same area. The very first partridge shoots on the light soils of East Anglia once supported early-winter densities of up to 350 birds per square kilometre: today the average is about 20. There is no mystery about how and why this has happened: the nemesis of the partridge population is the direct result of changes in agriculture and game management priorities. As a result there has grown up a whole generation of countrymen and sportsmen for whom the partridge is not a common game bird and may only be a comparatively unusual 'various' in the bag on shooting days which will be primarily devoted to pheasants. The shooting community in recent years can be divided into two broad camps – those who shake their heads and lament the loss of the once-abundant partridge, and those who feel that their numbers can be significantly restored by the development and application of practical game management techniques based on the intimate scientific understanding of partridge biology which now exists.

Jonathan Swift, the trenchant satirist of the age of Queen Anne, once wrote that mankind can be divided into two categories – those who expect the worst and those who hope for the best, and he described the latter as the nobler outlook. He also wrote in *Gulliver's Travels* that anyone who could make two ears of corn grow where only one had grown before would earn the thanks of society. We live in an age of agricultural overproduction and what Swift saw as a blessing has now become a major problem. But his two-for-one principle can also be applied to the challenge of restoring the partridge – an achievement which would delight the sportsman and would also mean the restoration of the habitat and conditions to promote many other forms of wildlife on Britain's farmland.

The cause of the grey partridge received what may prove to be its most important boost in recent years with the emergence of a group of environmentally conscious cereal farmers who have set up an important new long-term research experiment to assess the impact of agrochemical sprays and spraying techniques on farmland wildlife. The grey partridge is intimately associated with the arable farming scene and since its biology is now so well under-stood it makes an ideal 'indicator species' to monitor the effects on wildlife of agrochemicals and the ways they are used. The Game Conservancy's established expertise in this field led to their involvement in the co-ordination of what has become the Cereals and Gamebirds Research Project. This was inspired and funded by cereal farmers and is a tangible reproof of those who tend to dismiss all today's super-efficient cereal farmers as irresponsible profiteers, stripping the land of its assets and neglecting their stewardship of the farmland environment and the wildlife which lives there.

Farmer bashing has been a familiar theme in the environ-mental and conservation press since the 1960s, and not without some justification. The quest for higher yields and greater efficiency has often meant the loss of habitat with damaging effects upon a great many species of insects, wild flowers and birds. The changed agricultural scene has un-doubtedly been the sole cause of the decline of the grey partridge. But the setting up and funding of the Cereals and Gamebirds Project entirely from the purses of cereal growers and associated agricultural services is very encouraging, and indicates a growing willingness among farmers to examine the effects of their farming methods on wildlife and to work towards new and less injurious methods of maintaining good crop yields and also flourishing populations of many species of farmland plants, birds and animals. The grey partridge will not be the only beneficiary if a successful new cereal-growing strategy can be developed.

As this is written, preliminary results from the first two years' research are available. The laboratory testing of a range of agrochemicals, including insecticides, herbicides and fungicides, has taken place in parallel with field experiments with chemical sprays, in which their effects upon weedy plants, insects, butterflies, songbirds and game birds have all been monitored.

Partridges, as we have seen, are ground-nesters and prefer the cover of hedgerow bottoms. But cereal farmers have conventionally seen the hedges as a potential threat to the corn crop. They are reservoirs for many insects and a jumping-off point for the possible invasion of the crop by injurious insects and weeds. Consequently, where hedges have not been grubbed out altogether, the usual practice has been to spray the field right up to the field edge or headland, with herbicides to kill the grasses and weeds and insecticides to kill the aphids and other damaging insects. The consequences for partridge survival have been disastrous, with poorer nesting habitat in bare hedge bottoms and few insects for the chicks. There have been some benefits for the farmer in terms of increased yields and a cleaner crop, but what of the costs in terms of environmental damage? Is there a better way to balance productive farming and abundant wildlife?

An examination of cereal crops has shown that the headlands of the field are less productive than the middle, to the extent of a 30 per cent reduction in yield. The project scientists wanted to examine the effects of leaving some headlands unsprayed, and to compare them with other fields sprayed right up to the edges in the typical way. The modern spray-boom is 12 metres wide and its progress up and down the 'tram-line' tracks in growing cereal crops is a familiar sight in spring and early summer. Experiments were carried out by leaving 6-metre wide unsprayed strips along the headlands, on half the study area, and this was achieved by switching off one side of the spray boom. No sprays were applied to these strips after January, after general autumn treatment of all cereal fields with a herbicide to inhibit the growth and spread of weeds the following spring. Half the

9 *A selection of insects taken from the crops of young grey partridge chicks. Sawfly larvae, caterpillars and plant bugs are some of the most important sources of protein for the growing chicks, and if they have been eliminated by agrochemical sprays, chicks will have a low survival rate. Poor chick survival means a smaller harvestable surplus and poorer sport for the game shooter.*

study area was sprayed right up to the headlands as a 'control'.

The results after two seasons are exciting and potentially of the greatest importance for the future of the partridge and many other species. Grey partridge broods were significantly larger in the fields with unsprayed strips, averaging 10 chicks per brood, against 7·7 in the sprayed fields. The general chick survival rates in the two areas were also compared and in the sprayed fields just over one-third of the chicks survived to the age of ten days. Chicks in the unsprayed strips had almost twice the rate of survival.

These results from a cereal farm in north Hampshire were confirmed by other tests on eight farms in East Anglia. There brood size was, on average, up by almost 50 per cent on the unsprayed areas and the general rate of chick survival was slightly more than double that of the sprayed fields. Exciting results for those who would love to see the partridge making a real recovery in areas where it was once abundant!

What of the impact on farming? Does this restrained and modified spraying regime mean problems for the cereal farmer, with lower cereal yields and greater risks from insect damage and weed contamination? If this or any technique is agriculturally uneconomical it cannot be expected that cereal farmers will find it acceptable. The provisional answer at this early stage appears to be that crop yields are not measurably changed. The project scientists were able to announce unequivocally that 'there was no significant reduction in cereal yield as a result of leaving the headland unsprayed'. Contamination with weed seeds appears to be greater in the unsprayed headlands, as might be expected, but many of the smaller seeds can be removed by on-farm cleaning prior to the storage of the grain. This may be costly if weedy headlands have to be cut separately and the machinery later cleaned to remove weed seeds.

These and other costs and benefits will have to be analysed and assessed to decide whether a management strategy acceptable to cereal farmers can be developed. Only if the modified use of agrochemicals is economically viable can it be expected to gain general acceptance in the harsh climate of modern agronomics.

But what of other wildlife? The benefits to the partridge and the effects on the crop are not the end of the story. The sprayed and unsprayed areas were also monitored to see how butterflies, songbirds and other game birds fared. The results reveal the real potential of this sort of approach to cereal growing. Wild-breeding pheasants fared very much better in the unsprayed areas, with broods of more than twice the numbers of those on the sprayed areas. The non-native but well established red-legged partridge fared better too, with brood sizes benefiting considerably from unsprayed headlands. Although more research will clarify the effects, pre-

10 *A grey partridge's nest, well concealed in the thick cover at the bottom of a hedgerow. If the hen survives to hatch her brood, will the farmland environment be favourable for their survival? The cereal farmers' insecticides, herbicides and fungicides, if not wisely used, can destroy the insect life which is vital for partridge chicks, and for pheasants too.*

liminary indications are that numbers are up by about a third. Songbirds also seem to benefit from the greater availability of weed seeds in the unsprayed areas, but the response of butterflies has been particularly exciting. Seventeen species were found in both the sprayed and unsprayed headlands, and four additional species were seen only in the unsprayed ones. The density and occurrence of butterflies showed a very marked difference. Almost three times the number of butterflies of all species were found in the unsprayed headlands compared with the sprayed areas during the period from early May to mid-August.

These early results are quite dramatic and the implications for the future of cereal spraying methods and the welfare of many species of farmland wildlife are potentially enormous. These initial signs have given added impetus to the enthusiasm of those who believe that a management plan can be developed to restore the partridge and other declining farmland species without causing undue problems for the arable farmer.

If the unsprayed headlands are, as seems likely, an important step forward in partridge management, they can make a useful contribution only if they are accompanied by the maintenance of suitable nesting habitat for the birds and adequate control of predation at the critical spring nesting period. We return from the frontiers of this new research to the fundamental metaphor of the three-legged stool. Only if habitat, predator control and insect food supply are right can we expect to see an upswing in the fortunes of the grey partridge. All the signs are that it can be done. The blueprint exists and the first practical results confirm the theory. The fundamental question remains: does there exist the will to implement this blueprint for partridge survival?

4. *The Red-Legged Partridge*

On 21 March 1666 Samuel Pepys wrote in his diary: 'To the Duke of York. Sir Robert Long told us of the plenty of partridge in France, where he says the King of France and his company killed with their guns, in the plain de Versailles, three hundred and odd partridges at one bout.'

It is perhaps best to draw a discreet veil over how that particular bag of partridges was made, but it is safe to conclude that they were not shot on the wing. It is also likely that they were not the grey partridge, though it is indigenous to France and temperate mainland Europe, but the red-legged partridge (*Alectoris rufa*), or 'Frenchman'. This is a bird of dry and sandy habitats and its original range was in the more arid climates of the Mediterranean countries and in other closely related races eastwards across the Middle East and India. It has been established in many parts of France, Spain, Portugal, north-western parts of Italy and, of course, the British Isles.

Sir Thomas Browne, whose Continental travels and medical studies abroad had made him familiar with European wildlife, wrote in 1667, the year after Pepys's note, that Norfolk abounded with grey partridges 'yet the French red-legged is not to be met with', perhaps implying that some localised populations of this introduced species were already established in Britain. But the historical record remains obscure, although we know of attempts to establish the species in the royal parks at Windsor and Richmond in 1673, at Belvoir Castle in Leicestershire in 1682 and at Wimbledon in the reign of Queen Anne. By the end of the eighteenth century, however, we are on firmer ground, with many reports of well established red-leg populations in the Midlands, the eastern counties and East Anglia. The Victorian 'acclimatisers' tried to introduce the species to Ireland, where it failed, and it is only in the past twenty years that the species has established a toe-hold in parts of Northern Ireland and the Irish Republic, thanks to the enthusiasm of some game farmers and syndicate shoots and the support of the National Association of Regional Game Councils.

The red-leg has never been as popular a bird as the grey partridge and the response of sportsmen and gamekeepers was often downright hostile, especially in the last century. It was regarded as a pest on the finest partridge manors, was accused of fighting with the grey partridges and destroying their nests, and many a keeper would smash the eggs of a red-legged partridge if he found a nest on his rounds. Among the purist partridge shots there was considerable antipathy towards a bird which was apt to run off ahead of the beaters or a pointing dog instead of squatting and flushing like the grey partridge, and it was deemed to be a less sporting target and a rather poorer table bird too.

11   *The red-legged partridge is a bird of semi-arid Mediterranean regions, but has become well established in Britain since its introduction in the late 17th century. The wild population has been augmented by many major release programmes in recent years, including a number in Ireland.*

12 *The red-legged partridge usually produces two clutches of eggs, incubated separately by the cock and hen birds. When off the nest, red-legged partridges do not cover up their eggs and the risk of predation is therefore greater than with the well-concealed nests of grey partridges.*

Times and attitudes change and the red-leg is now firmly established across eastern, central and southern England, with smaller local populations in Scotland, eastern parts of Wales, and Ireland. Much of this can be attributed to the extensive rearing and releasing programmes of many shoots. The red-leg is comparatively easy to rear on the flock-mating principle and it is easier to hold the released birds on your ground. Released grey partridge may vanish very quickly by comparison. With the decline of the grey partridge, especially since the 1950s, anyone seeking early season partridge shooting has had to rely upon released red-legs for his sport – or else go abroad to places like Hungary and Spain. An estimated 800,000 red-legs are released each year in Britain and this has helped to maintain and increase the truly wild population, which has been in general decline since the 1970s, according to surveys by the Game Conservancy. There is general agreement that the species would probably fail to hold its own but for this annual topping-up with released birds.

A proportion of the released red-legs survive and breed but the status of the species is confused by the fact that a great many released birds have been hybrids between the red-leg and the chukar (*Alectoris chukar*). These hybrids are fertile and will interbreed. Their progeny revert over a few generations to the pure types. Taking the general country-wide situation, the pure red-leg seems to fare better than the chukar and most shoots where released hybrids have bred report that the stock eventually reverts to pure red-leg form, with the chukar influence being bred out.

The Wildlife and Countryside Act 1981 prohibited the release of these hybrids, although a five-year phasing-out period was agreed to enable game farmers to run down their hybrid stocks and concentrate on pure red-legs.

The red-leg partridge presents a very different appearance from that of the grey partridge. Apart from being rather larger, it is noticeably more striking in its plumage, with heavily barred flanks, a prominent black eye stripe with white above and a conspicuous white bib below, and, most notable of all, a vivid coral-red bill and legs.

In certain respects this species shares behavioural characteristics with the grey partridge. Both are monogamous and will pair for several years if both cock and hen survive that long, and they favour the light, drier soils of those parts of Britain where the grey partridge has always tended to flourish. But in many ways the red-leg is a very different bird from the smaller, more sombre native partridge. It is not only a bird of the open arable fields but will also make use of scrubland and the fringes of open woodland and will occasionally roost in trees and bushes, unlike the open-field 'jugging' of the grey partridge.

Research completed by the Game Conservancy in the early

1980s shed important new light upon the breeding behaviour of the red-legs, which are now known to break up their coveys and disperse into their breeding pairs rather later in the season than grey partridges. The male red-leg occupies and defends a home range, and is noticeably less aggressive towards his 'brothers' (other sibling cocks) than to unrelated males. The young females disperse from the family coveys to find a mate and settle in the home range which he has already chosen, and the spring dispersal of red-legs and their eventual density at nesting time is determined largely by the availability of adequate nesting habitat. The fewer the hedges, the further the birds will have to disperse to find a suitable breeding area, and there will be a lower density and a reduced shootable surplus for the sportsman as a consequence. The loss of good nesting cover, especially hedges removed in the trend towards larger fields, has affected the red-leg as well as his native counterpart.

The actual breeding strategy is where the two species differ most radically. Unlike the secretive grey partridge hen with her closely guarded and well concealed single nest, the red-leg often lays two clutches of eggs, the male incubating and brooding the first and the female the second. This happens with about 80 per cent of mature females and 20 per cent of young females. The average clutch is of about twelve eggs, rather smaller than the grey with its fifteen, and the birds do not deliberately cover up their eggs when they leave the nest. Even when ground cover in the form of grasses and other weedy growth is good, this habit inevitably leaves the unattended eggs vulnerable to predation by a variety of birds and mammals, and losses of eggs to predation occur at twice the daily rate of the grey partridge. But in most cases the double clutch system compensates for this high rate of loss and, in most seasons, the red-leg will produce about the same number of young as the grey partridge.

Once the eggs hatch the young chicks, like most game birds, are active and feeding for themselves. Their general diet comprises much the same range of food items as the grey partridge but the chicks are much less critically dependent

13 *Analysis of the droppings of partridge chicks has shown that the red leg chick is much less dependent upon insects in its diet than the grey partridge. But brood sizes are larger where insects are more abundant, thanks to restraint in the application of agrochemicals.*

upon insects. This important difference has been to their advantage in areas where agrochemical sprays have hit hard at the grey partridge chick survival rate. Young red-legs eat plant foods from the start and can survive and grow well on a diet of leaves, seeds and cereal grains, all of which figure prominently in their diet at a much earlier age than with grey partridges. But the use of herbicide sprays which kill much weedy growth can deprive them of weed seeds and the pre-liminary results of the Cereals and Gamebirds Project show that headlands left unsprayed with herbicides in spring seem to benefit red-leg chick survival, with brood sizes up by a third or so compared with those on sprayed areas.

Despite what many sportsmen have said about the rela-tively poorer sporting qualities of the red-leg compared with the grey partridge, there are many shoots where these birds are shown over the guns in a very exciting and testing way and the best red-leg shoots can provide sport of very high quality. But the behaviour and presentation of the birds is different from the grey partridge, where the covey tends to come forward as a unit, making it difficult for the guns to single out a target bird. The red-leg tends to split up and birds come forward singly, which greatly increases the likelihood of that individual bird being shot. This has also been seen in red grouse driving, where the adult birds tend to come over the butts singly and ahead of the younger birds in the covey, and driven grouse shooting harvests a high proportion of these older singletons. For coveys which stick closely to-gether as they come over the guns there is decidedly safety in numbers. When the grey partridge was abundant and shooting pressures high, those red-legs which came over the guns were twice as likely to be shot as the greys and under those circumstances the red-leg population could be seriously limited by shooting, although the efficient predator control on the old-style partridge shoots compensated by benefiting their breeding productivity. But on shoots where both species were present the red-leg was often outnum-bered by the grey partridge to the extent of 20 to 1.

Declining grey partridge numbers meant less partridge shooting generally and the red-leg then increased in numbers, reaching a one-to-one ratio with greys in some areas. Parts of the eastern counties of England recorded densities as high as 20 pairs per square kilometre in the late 1950s but there is evidence of a slight decline in wild stocks as the shooting of reared red-legs has grown in popularity since the late 1960s. The principal limiting factor for the species is not shooting pressure, which is not a significant factor for any British game species at present. Rather the problems lie with habitat loss, predator control and the modern style of tidy arable cropping, aided by agrochemical sprays. The three-legged stool principle is generally applicable to the red-leg, too, and the challenge for the management of the species in the future lies in ensuring that there is adequate nesting cover, suitable food and a degree of security from undue predation, especially at nesting time.

5. The Red Grouse

Grouse, more than any other game species, evoke a very clear mental picture of a certain type of landscape. The red grouse epitomises the heather moorland scenery of the uplands of Britain and Ireland which have traditionally been the stronghold of the species. In the public imagination there is a particular link between grouse and Scotland – heather, grouse, whisky, tartan, bagpipes and haggis mingling together in a familiar if rather music-hall association of all things Scottish, especially in the minds of those unfortunate enough not to be Scots. But in fact the most flourishing grouse populations and the biggest bags of shot grouse have always come from south of the border, especially in Lancashire, north Yorkshire and Co. Durham. Today, when grouse populations throughout the British Isles are under threat and in serious decline, it is the moors of northern England that are

14 *Grouse are widely distributed across the heather uplands of Britain and Ireland, but their numbers are in decline in almost all areas. Only the moors of Durham, north Yorkshire and Lancashire maintain really high grouse populations.*

---

the last bastions of grouse abundance. Other upland areas of Wales, Ireland and Scotland have all to a greater or lesser extent witnessed declines in their grouse numbers during this century. How and why this has happened is a complex question which no one fully understands. Only meticulous research and the development and implementation of radical moorland management strategies can provide the solution and help restore the fortunes of grouse across vast areas of the country where they were once abundant. Biologists and game managers can probably arrive at the means and the knowledge necessary to reverse the countrywide decline. Whether the will exists to implement these measures is something which only time will tell.

In all grouse areas the vital common factor is the presence of heather (*Calluna vulgaris*). The geographical distribution of grouse is directly related to that of heather-dominant vegetation, and it is impossible to overemphasise the importance of this plant for grouse. Its young shoots constitute well over 90 per cent of the diet of the adult birds, while longer mature heather provides them and their young with shelter from the weather, concealment from predators and, most important, safe nesting sites. Heather, of good quality and with the correct patterns of growth, represents the grouse's bed, board and breeding grounds. If in the future we are to have flourishing populations of grouse from which a shootable surplus can be harvested, providing sport for the guns and employment-generating income for the landowners, our heather uplands must be carefully conserved and maintained.

To mention income and to introduce the sordid business of money and economics into a discussion of grouse may be anathema to some of those who love the bird, its environment and the sport it provides. They are probably the sort of people who make infrequent, fair-weather trips to the moors but who otherwise live far removed from the realities of owning and managing hill ground in an age when pressures – economic, agricultural, environmental and social – are bringing about fundamental changes in the upland scene. Some experts warn that the ecological deterioration of our hills and moors is approaching crisis point; others aver that the situation has already passed the point of no return and that this environment has been irreversibly changed and irreparably damaged. One thing, however, is quite certain:

grouse and many other species of upland wildlife – animals, insects and plants – are seriously threatened by what has happened and is happening to the mountains, hills and moorland of these islands. The red grouse, with its aesthetic appeal, its sporting qualities and its economic importance, has become the principal 'indicator species' for monitoring these threatening changes and for developing remedial and preventive techniques which can be applied to stop the rot.

We have always been very proud of our grouse. Until recently it was almost impossible to pick up any written account of the bird without seeing the patriotic claim that this species was unique to the British Isles, our very own native game bird. In fact the taxonomists now tell us that our red grouse is only the British race or subspecies (*Lagopus lagopus scoticus*) of the willow ptarmigan or willow grouse (*Lagopus lagopus*), of which a total of sixteen subspecies have been identified across its range. This extends throughout the northern hemisphere, and usually north of latitude 55° N, in Europe, Asia and north America. But all these generations of patriotic, not to say xenophobic, sportsmen who proclaimed the uniqueness of *scoticus* were not entirely wrong, for it is the only subspecies which never develops any white plumage on its upper parts. All other races turn white in winter, most becoming almost entirely white apart from the distinctive dark tail feathers. Only the British and Irish populations remain wholly dark-coloured through the winter and in this respect at least our red grouse is unique. Unlike other *L. lagopus* subspecies, *scoticus* individuals moult progressively throughout the year and British grouse show enormous regional, seasonal and individual variations in plumage and colour types.

Irish and Hebridean grouse are generally paler than those in mainland Great Britain, which has given rise to occasional speculation that there may be a separate *hibernicus* subspecies, but the colour variation is explained by a different moulting pattern and a greater degree of winter feather growth in milder western areas. This seems to explain the colour variations which prompted naturalists like the

German Lutheran pastor Kleinschmidt to conclude that there was a quite distinct *hibernicus* form. In any event, any subspecific purity has been clouded by the numerous and frequent introductions of grouse into Ireland from Scotland and northern England.

Of great national and international importance is the British method of shooting grouse by driving the birds over lines of standing guns in butts. For more than a century this has been the standard shooting procedure in all areas where grouse numbers have been high enough to justify the construction of butts and the deployment of large and costly teams of beaters. Dogging over pointers and setters and walking up in line with spaniels and retrievers has tended to be confined to more marginal moors where grouse numbers have always been lower.

The international demand for driven grouse shooting is such that it has become quite the most expensive form of game shooting in this country. For a paying gun who buys top-quality grouse shooting each driven bird in the bag will cost him about £15–£23, compared with a unit cost of approximately £13 for pheasants and slightly more for partridges, based on 1985 average charges. The high prices which good grouse shooting commands are an eloquent compliment to the very high esteem in which the species is held as a sporting quarry. The revenue generated by marketing a large shootable surplus of grouse can be considerable – but it needs to be. The overheads are very high, the economics of grouse moor management are complex, and let no one be under any misapprehensions about its profitability. No landowner or anyone involved in the running of a grouse moor ever made a fortune from it. Countless worries and uncertainties, long hours and a modest living are the best that can be expected. Also grouse will represent only one factor in the multiple land use which is necessary for the continuing ecological and economic well-being of hill land, and even that is now gravely threatened by grouse decline. In many of our remote upland communities jobs will be lost and redundancies inevitable if the traditional environment is not

retained and grouse shooting ceases to make a real contribution to the various interlocking ways of exploiting the
land. The economic importance, both historical and contemporary, of grouse moors is perhaps best illustrated by the
fact that it led to the setting up of a major committee of
inquiry which reported in 1911; the Institute of Terrestrial
Ecology (formerly the Nature Conservancy) has devoted part
of its research unit at Banchory to grouse research; and
voluntary subscriptions by sportsmen and environmentalists have instigated a seven-year research project in the north
of England followed by a long-term investigation of Scotland's declining grouse stocks, carried out by the Game
Conservancy.

The life-cycle of grouse begins in the period September–
November, when adult cock birds begin to show signs of
taking up their territories. These territorial claims will almost
certain be temporarily disrupted by beaters, guns and
dogging parties on moors where shooting takes place
regularly in late August and September. By late October,
however, most moors will have finished their shooting
programme, although the legal season continues until 10
December. There are fewer hours of daylight and increasingly hostile weather, and when the daily bag size drops
below 35 brace or so it makes driven shoots uneconomical
and impracticable, while birds which have been repeatedly
disturbed by dogging or walking up will become less
approachable, often flushing wild and out of shot. Most moor
owners and shoot managers will therefore aim to have
completed their shooting before the end of October. The
'harvest' of surplus birds will leave an appropriate breeding
stock on the ground and as the final party of guns leaves the
moor when the last shoot is over they will be able to see cock
birds, conspicuous and proprietorial, on their territories.
Observation of marked individuals has shown that a cock
grouse which fails to secure a territory before the winter is
unlikely to be seen again or to survive until spring and
nesting time. He will be driven out by other territory-holding
males and will have to shift for himself, perhaps on un-

favourable marginal habitat where nutrition is poorer and where the risk of predation may be greater. For this reason the securing and maintaining of a territory is an essential prerequisite if adult male grouse are to contribute successfully to the population by finding a mate and producing a brood of young the following spring.

Ideally a breeding territory should contain a diversity of habitat types and this can best be achieved by managing the heather to provide a variety of ages and growth stages within an area of a few acres. There must be heather to give cover and shelter to the nest, if it is not to be open to bad weather and the eyes of predators. Shorter, younger heather, aged from four to eight years depending upon the rate of growth of the individual moor, provides the succulent green shoots with their relatively high protein content which is critical to grouse in spring and makes up the overwhelming bulk of the diet of adult grouse throughout the year. The nutritional value of the heather will depend upon the soil type, which in its turn is a function of the underlying geological structure of the moor. The best-quality heather in terms of its growth rate and nutritional value to grouse occurs on well drained moors in limestone or basalt areas where the rainfall is not more than 35 inches per year. These criteria tend generally to be met on the eastern moors of northern England and Scotland. Acidic and less nutritious heather, often on ill drained blanket peat with a granite bedrock and high annual rainfall, is at the other end of the spectrum and characterises many upland areas in the wetter western areas, including the western Highlands and the Hebrides, and much of Ireland and Wales. Such areas generally do not sustain populations of grouse at anything like the density of the best moors.

To ensure that the optimum diversity of heather types with plenty of 'edges' is available to large numbers of cock grouse, each holding a relatively small territory, the heather is usually managed by rotational burning. Muirburn in late autumn and early spring gets rid of old, rank, woody heather which has gone past the 'stage of providing deep, dense nesting cover, and burning will quickly be followed by regeneration,

15 *The heather habitat upon which grouse depend is best managed by rotational burning, to provide young shoots as food and longer growth for nesting cover and as a refuge from predators. Burning in long narrow strips creates an ideal patchwork of heather of various ages, and grouse like the 'edge effect' where longer heather gives way to new growth. Other species of upland birds also benefit from this moorland environment, now threatened in many areas by afforestation or over-grazing by sheep.*

with new heather growth emerging within a year. Growth rates vary from moor to moor and intelligent management will organise burning so as to create a patchwork of heather areas of varying ages, from new emerging growth to mature, deep heather. Small patches of an acre or two can often be difficult to burn and the widely adopted alternative is to burn in long strips, which may be of almost any length but should not be more than 30 yards wide. Grouse are reluctant to feed out onto large areas of short heather and always prefer to be able to scuttle quickly under cover in the shelter of long heather. This is one of the things which makes edges so important. Strips of shorter heather not more than 30 yards wide mean that a grouse will never find itself feeding more than 15 yards from the edge of secure cover and a hen grouse with her brood will be able to rush them quickly to safety.

Heather burning needs to be carried out with care and precision. A fast downwind burn may get out of control, and in its swift progress may only burn off the superficial growth, failing to destroy the tougher woody stalks and the mat of heather debris which litters the surface of the ground under long heather. This debris often promotes a damp micro-climate which can harbour ticks; the vigorous growth of new heather will be inhibited if a mat of litter remains after the fire. A slow, steady burn is much better, removing all old growth and heather debris and leaving a beneficial ash residue to enrich the soil and promote new growth. 'Back-burning', working the fire slowly upwind, can be a useful tactic to produce a hotter fire and a more complete burn. Although all heather regenerates from seed and not from roots, excessive heat can scorch the ground, slowing the rate of new growth or even sterilising the peat, and in extreme cases can set fire to blanket peat. Members of a burning party working upwind must take special precautions against the heat, smoke and sparks by wearing masks and visors, but gloves should not be worn. When the hands become uncom-fortably hot it is time to back off, to avoid the risk of clothing becoming scorched. This can and does happen, and some exposed areas of skin act as a useful thermometer to protect those involved in muirburn from the potentially serious results of excessive heat from heather fires.

Heather habitat requires not only this abundance of healthy multi-aged growth and the edge effect which is created where short, recently burnt heather meets longer, older growth. Research has shown that other things are necessary to create optimum conditions. Grouse need help to digest their fibrous staple diet, and small, rough particles of grit provide a natural medium for cutting, grinding and macerating the heather shoots. If grit is not immediately available grouse may fly quite a distance to find it, and on moors of blanket peat with little or no exposed rock this may be necessary. Hill tracks and roadsides are favourite gritting places, especially in the mornings and evenings, but grouse will respond well if small piles of grit are put out here and there across the moor. This may be totally unnecessary on moors where there is enough exposed rock and natural grit, but can be definitely beneficial where natural grit is scarce.

Gritting and burning are not new concepts to grouse keepers, but the importance of insects in the diet of young grouse chicks is something which has recently come to prominence. Its importance has been demonstrated only in recent years, principally by experiments in Yorkshire as part of the Game Conservancy's upland research work. The value of insects to another game bird, the grey partridge, is nothing new: decades of research have confirmed that inadequate insect food can decimate partridge chick numbers and post-war agricultural methods have often reduced insect numbers on farmland to such a low level that grey partridge populations have simply gone to the wall. But the twentieth-century literature on grouse and their food is almost silent on the subject of insects and grouse chicks. This is curious, in view of the findings of Percy Grimshaw, the insect expert who worked for the Lovat Committee Inquiry on Grouse Disease before the First World War. He recorded in those massive volumes, published in 1911, that 'the food of young grouse is largely made up of insects'. A. S. Leslie, the secretary to the Lovat Committee, also noted from his own observations that broods of young chicks favour 'rushes and long grass in the more swampy parts of the moor. This is specially noticeable in very dry seasons. Whether the chicks seek these damp spots for the sake of shelter from the heat or in quest of insect life is not known'.

There seems to have been no follow-up until some studies on grouse chicks were carried out by the Grouse Research Unit of the Institute of Terrestrial Ecology at Banchory. Post-mortem examination of grouse chicks from some of Scotland's north-eastern moors showed they contained some insect food – about 5 per cent, measured as dry weight – but inevitably an examination of dead chicks could not shed any

16 *This grouse was caught on a north Yorkshire moor and wing-tagged as a small chick. Now, as a year-old adult hen, she is fitted with a radio to enable her movements and breeding success to be monitored. Radio tracking has shown that hen grouse will lead their chicks to damp 'bog flushes' where they will feed voraciously on insects like craneflies.*

light on whether or not insects helped grouse chick survival, and if so by how much. From 1982 onwards Game Conservancy scientists followed the development of grouse chicks using the miniaturised radio transmitters which have become such important aids to game research in the field. Hen grouse fitted with radio tags were tracked and it was a comparatively simple matter to get a succession of directional fixes at night on a roosting hen and her brood of chicks. The intersection of the fix-lines marked the roosting site and the chicks' droppings were collected the following morning – a similar procedure to the study of pheasants and partridges on lowland study areas.

Microscopic examination of the droppings revealed what foods the chicks had been eating, and both insect and plant remains could be detected. Craneflies or daddy-long-legs had been found in Grimshaw's earlier studies and the 1980s study confirmed that these occur frequently in the diet of young grouse. A range of other insects was found to be included in the chicks' bill of fare, including small flies and certain wasps. Sawflies, in both the caterpillar and adult stages, click beetles, various caterpillar larvae of lepidopteran species, ichneumon wasps, various small flies and craneflies all occurred in 40 per cent or more of the samples examined. It is also significant that these insects tend to be those which are conspicuous to the young grouse chicks, moving relatively slowly through the heather and other vegetation, and easily spotted and caught by the young grouse.

The availability of these insects is also a matter of critical timing. They tend to emerge more or less simultaneously in the moorland environment, and it is significant that this abundance of insect life becomes available at the very time when growing grouse require protein and certain amino-acids which build proteins. The abundance of these insects reaches its peak in the early days of June, when most grouse chicks have hatched and are, on a rough average, about two weeks old. Radio-tagging showed that grouse chicks tend not to wander far afield during the first two days after hatching but that subsequently hens and their broods might venture quite far and wide, with successive overnight roosts up to a quarter of a mile apart. The biologists found that hen grouse and their broods showed a decided preference for wet areas, boggy flushes and patches of sphagrium moss. Heather seems to be less favoured, especially when it is young or recently burnt, and wet flushes and sphagnum bogs tend to be very much richer in insect life than young, short heather. But sphagnum moss beds and wet places do not represent the best cover either from bad weather or predators, and it is assumed that they are chosen primarily for their food value.

These closely studied grouse chicks were clearly feeding on relatively large amounts of insects, but does this diet promote better growth and a higher rate of chick survival? After all, chick survival is the key to the production of a harvestable shootable surplus in any game bird species. When chick survival is low there will be, in the sportsman's terms, a poor breeding season and a reduced surplus for the guns. Conversely, a high rate of chick survival will lead to an abundance of young birds and an ample shootable surplus. This is good news not only for the sportsman but also for the landowner. A self-renewing and adequately large game harvest will maintain the capital value and the annual income of his land, enabling him to continue employing gamekeepers and other estate workers whose jobs would otherwise disappear. Most important of all, it ensures the continuance of traditional patterns of upland land use and management which maintains an internationally important environment for a whole range of moorland wildlife, plants and insects.

Grouse are fast-growing, short-lived birds, fully grown within less than three months after hatching, breeding in their first spring and usually dead before the age of two. The fast, healthy growth of grouse chicks depends upon their intake of certain necessary substances. Chicks need phosphorus and nitrogen, and research at Banchory has shown that young grouse will select young heather shoots which are rich in these nutrients. But insects provide an even richer source of the chemical 'building blocks' for the proteins which the growing birds need. Heather is a relatively poor source of this important growth aid and grouse chicks would need to eat vast quantities of it to achieve a reasonable intake. Captive chicks which had access to abundant insect food were invariably bigger and heavier than others which only ate a few insects, while chicks feeding on heather alone simply died. These experimental observations confirmed the value of insects and, by implication, the importance of the damp bog flushes where insect numbers are highest. This has an obvious bearing on the application of drainage schemes to moors.

Heather likes dry conditions, and its growth may be improved by drainage. Generous grants are available for the cutting of drainage channels or 'grips' to encourage faster and more complete water run-off in upland areas, but the benefits which may result for the rate of heather growth and regeneration must be weighed against possible losses, if drainage dries out bog flushes and reduces insect numbers, especially during that critical period in late May and June. But drainage schemes may not in fact be a major threat since grips often become blocked as the sides cave in, thereby creating new bog flushes. There may even be a case for encouraging this blocking of grips on dry moors where there are few damp areas and a shortage of insects.

Before insects can benefit the growing grouse chicks, there must first be a healthy breeding stock of adult grouse which have overwintered well and are in the correct physical condition to produce good clutches of fertile eggs. Once hatched, the young chicks' fate will be determined largely by habitat, food availability, parasites, disease, predators and the condition of the hen bird; but a vigorous and fertile breeding population is the natural prerequisite.

Grouse are short-lived birds and a good example of a game species which completes its life-cycle of birth, reproduction and death fairly quickly. If all the conditions are at their best, grouse will produce sufficient young to give an adult-to-juvenile ratio in August of almost 4 to 1. This represents an approximate brood size of eight chicks to each adult pair and such a high young-to-old ratio will provide a large harvestable surplus for shooting. Limiting factors like disease, weather and predation will also remove a proportion of the population, but disease can also play a part in regulating grouse numbers. Two diseases, louping-ill and strongylosis, have been studied in some detail in recent years.

Louping-ill is a virus disease which is all too familiar to hill sheep farmers, especially in parts of Scotland. It attacks the sheep's central nervous system, causing it to 'loup' or stagger and lose muscular co-ordination and normal freedom of movement. (Its effects are comparable to those of polio-myelitis in humans.) It is transmitted by the sheep tick (*Ixodes ricinus*) and will also attack grouse. Ticks are catholic in their tastes and will attach themselves to almost any vertibrate host, principally mountain hares and roe deer, but the louping-ill virus only has a critically serious effect upon sheep and grouse. Dipping sheep, especially in midsummer and autumn, can destroy sheep-borne ticks but the ticks and the louping-ill virus can persist even in sheep-free areas, where its persistence is attributable to grouse alone. A major factor in maintaining unduly high densities of ticks seems to be the depth of the mat of heather litter and other undecayed vegetation which exists above the surface of the soil or peat. Ticks live in this damp mat layer when they are not on one of the host animals, and the deeper the mat the higher the humidity and the higher the survival rate of the ticks. Muirburn, as we have mentioned, can help reduce or destroy the mat and deprives the ticks of a favourite habitat. More research into louping-ill continues and we need to know a great deal more about the roles played by all the various tick host species in spreading the infected ticks. It seems, however, that ticks are not in themselves a threat to grouse and will not produce noticeably adverse effects in grouse populations, except when louping-ill is present, or where the grouse are in poor physical condition. This is the case in many parts of Scotland, where good moors have been ruined by the disease. As yet, the stronghold of high grouse populations in northern England remains largely free from louping-ill.

Strongylosis, however, is another matter. The problem has been known and discussed for well over a century, especially on the better moors, where grouse regularly achieve high densities. 'Grouse disease' caused by parasitic worms was first recognised in 1854 and two approaches to the problem developed. Sir Ralph Payne-Gallwey, one of the most famous Victorian 'big shots', believed that disease broke out in spring two years after a bumper, high-density year. The Lovat Committee took a different view, concluding that grouse disease only strikes when heather quality has deteriorated, especially when it has been badly frosted. This was the reported conclusion, despite the important work on strongylosis carried out by the principal field observer for the Lovat Inquiry, Edmund Wilson, who is best remembered as the scientist for Scott's Antarctic expedition. He perished on that ill fated venture and work on grouse disease did not

17 *An electron microscope reveals how strongyle threadworms have attacked the caeca or 'blind guts' of a grouse. Strongylosis can be a major cause of low fertility and poor chick productivity among grouse, especially on moors where grouse densities are high.*

begin again in earnest until scientific study began again in the late 1970s.

Strongylosis is the massive infection of the caeca or 'blind guts' by the tiny threadworm *Trichostrongylus tenuis*. This infection begins when grouse eat heather containing the strongyle larvae. These develop and build up in the caeca of the host and bring about a general deterioration in the bird's physical condition. Most important, the disease reduces the fertility of the hen birds, which lay fewer eggs and at a slower rate than worm-free birds. These facts emerged from a study of captive birds at the Banchory research unit in the 1970s and highlighted the need for more detailed work on this disease and its effects on grouse populations. Obviously, any disease which leads to reduced breeding success means fewer grouse and a smaller surplus of shootable birds. This in turn affects the economic viability of grouse moors, which must be maintained if the deterioration of Britain's upland habitat is to be avoided.

Infected grouse play a part in the strongyle worm's life-cycle by excreting its eggs in the caecal droppings. These are different in appearance from the normal droppings, which are long, cylindrical and fibrous in texture. Caecal droppings are soft and look like chocolate mousse, and those deposited by a strongyle-infested grouse contain eggs which will develop through the embryo stage, to be eaten by other grouse feeding on larvae-bearing heather, thus completing the cycle. Recent studies on moors in the north of England have shown that, on average, a worm burden of 4,000 is enough to bring about a physical deterioration in the individual bird. It has been suggested this is because strongylosis inhibits the bird's intake of protein. The higher the worm count, the greater the impact on fertility, and in extreme cases the bird will die. What is the link between this disease and the massive fluctuations in grouse numbers which can occur from year to year? How can strongylosis be controlled so as to improve grouse productivity and maintain the economic well-being of heather uplands where grouse shooting is the principal form of land use?

It has often been suggested that grouse numbers fluctuate in cycles and that this accounts for situations such as, for example, a shootable surplus of 3,000 brace in a season dropping within two or three years to perhaps only 300 brace, and back up again to a four-figure total after another year or two, all on the same moor. Fortunately, sportsmen and moor owners have always tended to keep detailed game books. From these, many of which give unbroken records going back over a century, biologists have been able to trace the historical fluctuations in grouse densities as indicated by the numbers shot from season to season. The results seem to show that grouse do not conform to a simple cyclic pattern but are 'quasi-cyclic' – they undergo irregular patterns of fluctuation caused by the combination of two factors.

18 *This hen grouse has a very prominent breastbone and reveals all the signs of weakness and emaciation typical of strongylosis. Recent experiments have shown that grouse can be caught and dosed to eliminate the strongyle worms and restore their health, fertility and reproductive success.*

Density-related disease may tend to cause definite and fairly regular cycles of abundance and scarcity but this pattern is upset by random factors such as variations in the weather or the incidence of disease at nesting time in the unpredictable spring climate of Britain's uplands. The weather is beyond anyone's control but if we can get to grips with a disease which periodically causes these massive crashes in grouse numbers there are exciting implications for grouse-moor management and land use in the uplands. If moor managers can control disease and overcome disease-related deaths and infertility, that will iron out and help stabilise part of the wildly fluctuating situation which has traditionally meant bumper seasons and lean years following one another in quick succession.

Tests and studies of grouse living free on Yorkshire moors

have been very revealing. Since 1982 numbers of hen grouse have been caught up by dazzling the birds with a bright light at night in early spring. Some are treated orally with an anti-worm drench which will rid them of strongyle worms; others are merely 'dosed' with distilled water. The latter exercise provides a 'control' group, which undergoes the same stresses of catching up and handling but is not been treated with any medication. Both groups of hen grouse were fitted with miniature radio transmitters – a godsend to the field biologist.

Treated and untreated birds were tracked and their breeding success monitored. Three years of this work confirms that worm-free grouse lay more eggs, hatch more chicks and rear larger broods of young than untreated, worm-bearing birds. Catching and handling make no difference to the breeding success of the untreated birds when compared with other wild and unhandled individuals.

The way in which strongylosis reduces grouse fertility and productivity was revealed by the fact that in one year infected birds produced clutches of eggs averaging 5·8 in number, while treated, worm-free hens laid an average of 8·0. These larger clutches had a 75 per cent rate of hatching success, twice as good as the 38 per cent achieved by the untreated control hens. After hatching, the first ten days of life are critically important, and 58 per cent of chicks from dosed mothers survived to this age, more than twice the rate of the control chicks at 27 per cent. These are striking figures and they prove how strongylosis can drastically affect the productivity of grouse. With driven grouse shooting commanding a market price on let shooting days of £40 or more per brace, the size of the shootable surplus can make an enormous difference to the economics of running a grouse moor. As things stand today, grouse-moor management as one component of multiple upland land use often teeters on the verge of profitability and at best the income on major assets and investments is uncertain and highly variable. Preliminary estimates indicate that, at average 1985 rates, control of strongylosis may be worth upwards of £5 per acre per annum on moors in the north of England. On a moor of only 5,000 acres that means an increase of £25,000 – a major boost to the economics of the moor and one which also makes a long-term contribution to capital values. Anything which can be done to maintain a more consistent level of productivity from a vigorous, disease-free breeding stock will help to ensure a more secure future for grouse and the habitat which they share with so many other upland species.

Strongylosis, about which we have learned a great deal more in recent years, is only one of several threats to grouse abundance. Grouse must be seen in the wider context of the general upland environment and the many changes which have taken place there, especially since the Second World War. Areas of coniferous afforestation, bracken and grassland are increasing, while the areas where heather remains the dominant vegetation are diminishing. What has brought about this trend?

Sheep farming is a well established activity on hill land. Sheep and grouse can enjoy a harmonious coexistence where moors are managed thoughtfully and for the benefit of both. But we know grouse to be heavily dependent upon a heather-dominated habitat, and changes in the density of sheep stocking, grazing pressure and techniques of husbandry have conspired to bring about a decline in the heather over much of Britain and Ireland. Sheep were formerly stocked at a relatively lower density than today. They were shepherded in the traditional way and they spread and grazed evenly over the moors. Recent changes have meant that many moors now have a much higher stocking rate, largely owing to the payment of a headage subsidy on every ewe on the hill.

Sheep graze selectively and prefer the more palatable fescues and bent grasses. These are eventually grazed out or die back with the onset of winter, and heather then becomes the mainstay of the sheep's winter diet. It is an evergreen, readily accessible even when snow covers the hills, and sheep will adopt home ranges over which their grazing will take place. If they graze evenly over a moor sheep are beneficial to the heather, and thus to the grouse, by encouraging new growth and maintaining the heather in a state which suits both sheep and grouse. Sheep husbandry and flourishing grouse populations can coexist well in this way.

However, Britain's sheep numbers have increased and the national flock has doubled since 1947. In certain areas like the Peak District numbers have trebled over the past fifty years. Sheep tend also to be kept on the hills for longer periods, often all year round, with tupping and lambing now carried out on the open moors. Such flocks are usually given supplementary feed in the form of hay or feed blocks. This supplementary food is an important contribution to the lambing productivity of hill ewes, for good feeding, especially just before and after mating, usually means a bigger crop of lambs. Feed blocks and hay are especially important when the winter weather is bad. The sheep which concentrate at feeding areas will graze and trample the surrounding heather and damage it seriously. Hay is often put out daily close to vehicle tracks and is frequently spread over long heather, which prevents it blowing away. Sheep naturally concentrate on these 'fothering' sites, often gathering there hours before the hay vehicle arrives. Grazing and trampling combine to kill the heather, and the farmer's response is to continue fothering on other areas of heather, which eventually suffer the same fate. These two factors – higher densities of sheep stocking and the concentration of sheep at supplementary feeding sites – have brought about serious heather decline on many moors. To talk of optimum stocking rates is meaningful only when the grazing pressure is evenly distributed over the moor, and high concentrations of sheep at feeding sites are very destructive of heather.

Intense and sustained grazing pressure may eventually destroy the heather and what was once a heather-dominated grouse moor becomes permanent grass or 'white ground'. When this happens the heather can be restored only by intensive and costly management, involving the removal of all grazing stock, heather planting, spraying to eradicate bracken and other measures. High densities of sheep may exert another destructive influence on moors, for their hooves can cut away at the peat, eroding it and destroying areas which would otherwise be protected from erosion by the binding action of plants like heather. Eventual loss of the heather is a serious matter for both sheep and grouse. Sheep lose their staple winter diet and must either suffer a serious food shortage or be even more reliant upon supplementary feed. Grouse quite simply lose their essential habitat. Afforestation with conifers – probably non-indigenous species like Sitka spruce planted in large, even-aged mono-cultures – may then be undertaken as the only viable use for land which has been devalued both environmentally and economically in this way.

Afforestation of hill land has become an increasingly common feature of the countryside, especially in the northern and western areas of the British Isles. There are attractive tax incentives and other financial benefits for the private landowner, quite apart from the Forestry Com-mission's country-wide planting activities, and many upland proprietors have already committed themselves to major afforestation programmes. Many more will follow if the traditional multiple use of moorland should become un-economical, and yet more tens of thousands of upland acres will be ploughed and planted with fast-growing softwood trees like lodgepole pine and Sitka spruce. These plantations are, at best, a very mixed blessing for wildlife in general, and a decided disadvantage for traditional upland birds like the grouse. To give only one instance, forestry blocks always tend to harbour foxes, crows and other predators, and these jeopardise the survival and breeding success of ground-nesting birds on adjacent moorland.

When the forester's plough turns over the peat and prepares the ground for planting, grouse may not be adversely affected straight away. In fact they seem to respond well in the immediate aftermath of ploughing and planting, when old heather has been ploughed in, new growth is encouraged and many aspects of the environment are briefly freshened up by the disturbance. Grouse will live and breed in new plantations, sometimes remaining even when the young trees have grown waist-high. Then they will forsake the area permanently, and the effect of afforestation will have been to displace the grouse and other species like snipe, golden plover and dunlin for ever. There may be a relatively brief period when young conifer plantations benefit black-game, and the spread of capercaillie too has been helped by afforestation, but its effects have, on balance, been seriously detrimental to grouse and other upland species which are adapted to live in open habitats where the vegetation is short and usually heather-dominated. Waders, like snipe and golden plover, are known to avoid areas near forest edges, thus impoverishing the bird life of many smaller unplanted areas of open moor.

Forestry has other effects too, which may be less immediately obvious. If a forest borders a grouse moor it will almost certainly interfere with the heather-burning strategy on that moor. No keeper or moor owner wants to run the risk of a fire getting out of control and destroying the trees. Compensation claims for a really serious forest fire might run to hundreds of thousands of pounds, and many proprietors and shooting tenants now insure against it, paying high annual premiums which place a further financial burden on the business of maintaining a good grouse moor. Inevitably the tendency is to play safe and not to burn in the vicinity of plantations, with the result that heather deteriorates in those areas. To this must be added the tendency, already mentioned, of predators like foxes, stoats, feral cats and corvids to frequent forestry blocks, which increases the pressures of predation of adjacent areas of moorland. Effective habitat management and predator control become very difficult and so the grouse decline.

The extent of this problem is dramatically illustrated by the fact that Great Britain has lost over two million acres of moorland since 1946, and over half that loss has taken place over the last ten years. Some land has been lost through reclamation and improvement but where rainfall is high and the geology is not conducive to rich soils the trend has been entirely towards forestry. This has meant radical changes in the upland environment and its animal and plant life which are positively bad for grouse.

'One good moor helps another' is a useful epigram for expressing what happens when a well managed grouse moor is surrounded by others of similar quality. Bag records show that well keepered moors which march with other well maintained shoots to form large, continuous areas of tens or even hundreds of thousands of acres of heather-dominated moorland will support higher populations of grouse and other upland birds and a larger harvest of shootable birds than isolated moors where there is little or no keepering on adjacent land. The piecemeal planting of conifers has broken up the upland landscape and where as recently as a generation ago the vistas were of uninterrupted heather moors, today the hills of north and western Britain and Ireland present a more or less random picture of softwood plantations, 'white ground' and other recently reclaimed stretches of principally grassy vegetation, and areas which are still retained primarily as multi-purpose grouse moors with hill sheep. All the evidence points to this as a damaging development for grouse and other upland birds, restricting the extent of heather-dominated land and leading to a lower and less efficient level of heather management and predator control. Although the grouse is only one species in a wider and more complex equation, it is a particularly important one.

More than any other upland bird the red grouse has a tangible economic value. Large upland areas are owned by proprietors who either bought or inherited them as being primarily grouse moors. In late Victorian and Edwardian days the shooting of driven grouse reached its peak, and that form of land use predominated in many parts of northern England and Scotland. It gave employment not only to moor keepers but to countless other estate workers who helped in the running of sporting properties. Social structures have changed and estates and other upland properties now give employment to far fewer staff. Rising labour costs, changes in taxation and the effects of mechanisation are only some of the many factors which have brought this about. Where top-quality grouse shooting is still available it commands premium prices but the country-wide trends are downwards. More and more estates have been forced to reconsider their position as grouse stocks have dwindled, and there inevitably comes a point where the sporting income is so reduced that economic estate management compels proprietors to consider the two principal alternatives of intensive hill sheep farming or commercial timber growing.

Unlike either of these, the grouse does not attract a subsidy or any tax benefits. On the contrary, it adds the additional burden of sporting rates to the other outgoings of Scottish properties, and on moors where grouse numbers have fallen seriously this is often the last straw. For an estate owner to see his annual grouse harvest and the revenue it generates decline relentlessly is bad enough. To receive sporting rate demands, based on an earlier five-year-average assessment when bags were perhaps ten times larger, really rubs salt into the wound. To pay thousands of pounds annually in sporting rates on so many brace of non-existent grouse which are bureaucratically deemed to have been shot is intolerable to Scottish landowners, many of whom have already suffered the distress of seeing their grouse virtually disappear despite their very best endeavours to maintain optimum standards of moor management and keepering. To give only one small but typical example, I can think of a small property in Ross-shire where, despite continued keepering and heather burning and no increase in sheep stocking, the annual bag of grouse has fallen to around 20 brace. Rates are still payable on over 150 brace per annum, based on the average bags in the late 1970s. Many estates like this have already abandoned grouse as part of their traditional management structure, regarding them more as a liability than an asset. When heather management and predator control cease and intensive grazing or afforestation comes to dominate what was formerly a grouse moor, the grouse is not the only species to suffer. With it goes a whole interlocking system of upland wildlife, and that fact is increasingly recognised by environmentally minded organisations and individuals who are probably otherwise ill disposed towards game shooting and field sports in general. In the uplands, as elsewhere in the British Isles, conservationists and sportsmen are becoming increasingly aware of the vital role which game management has played in the conservation of habitats vital to many species of birds, animals, insects and plants.

Grouse populations fluctuate, as has been discussed in connection with strongylosis, and optimistic Scottish moor owners have pinned their hopes on a revival in grouse numbers after the decline which has taken place in recent years. But an upswing has not come and the situation is now critical, especially for estates which are geared up and have budgeted in the traditional way for grouse shooting as a principal income earner. In response to the needs of Scotland's landowners and the deep concern of environmentalists generally, the Game Conservancy has undertaken a major research project on Scottish grouse, to seek to identify the causes of the decline, the influences which have prevented grouse numbers from recovering, and if possible to devise practical measures to reverse the trend and restore grouse populations.

If this can be done it will not merely represent the saving of many once-productive grouse moors, the employment they provide, the influx of free-spending tourists into remote rural areas, and the improvement in the capital values of upland estates, desirable though these may be. It will have a much more fundamental effect for a wide variety of fauna and flora, and for the face of Britain's uplands. If our traditional moorland ecology is to be retained the grouse moors must remain productive and economically viable. If that can be achieved it will be an incalculably valuable contribution to our heritage of wildlife on the hills and moors.

The scale of the problem is very large and the project represents an enormous challenge. Before research in the field can begin (and it is about to start as these words are written) the project biologists must know the background to the problems they are tackling. Like doctors, they must be aware of the nature and extent of the symptoms before they can tackle the ailment effectively. Accordingly, a large-scale survey of the historical bag records of Scotland's grouse, and of other upland quarry species too, was undertaken in 1984. Scotland has about 350 grouse moors and data were obtained from 48 per cent of these. This sample of almost half the total provides a fairly reliable statistical picture, and the figures which emerged from an analysis of bag records, which often went back a century or more, are very alarming. Sadly, even these are an underestimate of the true extent of the decline of Scotland's grouse, since many owners whose land is now afforested or where, for whatever reason, grouse are no longer shot did not submit their bag records for earlier seasons.

Scotland has lost over 70 per cent of its red grouse stocks in the classic grouse-moor areas of Tayside and Grampian since the outbreak of the Second World War. Dumfries and Galloway, though always a less productive region, has lost over 80 per cent, while the Borders has been least hard hit, but has still suffered a decline of about 40 per cent. It is a grim picture.

The meticulous bag records kept by almost all estates have made it possible to trace the fluctuating fortunes of Scotland's grouse populations, which are directly related to the numbers shot each season. The golden age of Scottish grouse shooting lasted from late Victorian times until 1938, after which a decline took place from which the population never really recovered. This was the first of two downward steps and it meant a reduction on the Perthshire moors from an annual average of 66 grouse shot per square kilometre in 1920–38 to 34 grouse in the period 1970–5. The Grampian region, with its celebrated moors, had averages over the same period of 62 grouse and 38 grouse respectively. In Dumfries and Galloway the inter-war period produced an average of 34 grouse per square kilometre, with a drop to 18 grouse in the years 1970–5.

That first step was serious and, in very general terms, meant a country-wide drop of about 50 per cent in Scotland's grouse harvest. But most moors remained viable, producing depleted but still adequate annual harvests of grouse to supply the demands of sportsmen and to make grouse shooting still a financially sound form of land use. But the figures for the period 1976–83 make sorry reading. Those classic Tayside moors crashed by about another 70 per cent, from 34 to 14 grouse per square kilometre; Grampian moors were down from averages of 38 to 22 grouse; while Dumfries and Galloway fell on average from 18 to just 6 grouse per square kilometre. Only the Borders moors, with an average drop from 41 to 30 grouse, have escaped the very worst of this recent decline.

As mentioned earlier in connection with late-season grouse driving, daily bags of less than 35 brace (70 head) of grouse make driven days uneconomical and generally unsatisfactory. The deployment of large numbers of beaters, flankers and many other key personnel, all of whom have to be paid a realistic daily wage, becomes too costly. Paying guns become dissatisfied with smaller bags, which may entail frequent blank drives and little or no sport for some of the party – a rather dreary day's shooting, in fact. Small bags will, at best, lead to a change from driving, with the premium prices it commands, to walking up and dogging, when guns pay half as much at most. With much revenue lost, keepers will have to be redeployed on other estate work or even made redundant. Habitat management and predator control will deteriorate still further until grouse shooting of any sort is eventually discontinued altogether.

Scotland's serious predicament elicits a sinking feeling of *déjà vu* in anyone who witnessed what happened to Ireland's grouse populations in the late 1960s. Although most of Ireland's moors were never, even in their heyday, more than marginal grouse areas by comparison with those of Scotland and northern England, populations were still sufficient to provide good sport, usually over setters and pointers, with some well favoured areas sustaining sufficient grouse to make driving feasible. A slow country-wide decline began early this century, although well managed moors continued to produce good annual harvests of grouse up to the last war.

A County Antrim moor of which I was the shooting tenant in the 1970s recorded some 80-brace days in the 1920s and the average bags for only a few driven days each season in the 1930s were around 400 brace. By the 1960s very heavy sheep stocking had ruined much of the heather, despite which the moor still produced about 40–50 brace a season to two guns shooting rather casually over setters. By 1975 the season's total had crashed to just 3½ brace and it has never recovered. Annual spring censuses with pointers and setters to count the nesting birds have shown that only five or six pairs of grouse now nest on the entire 2,000-acre moor.

All over Ireland the same story could be told. The 1950s and 1960s saw Irish grouse numbers depleted from their pre-war abundance but they appeared to be stable at levels which meant that two guns pottering about on hill land and the lower heathery blanket bogs could expect to come home with a bag of 5–8 brace. The 1967 season showed a noticeable upswing in grouse numbers but it was only to be a flash in the pan. Within five years most moors lost 90 per cent of their grouse.

The reasons for this have never been satisfactorily explained. Grouse in Ireland had never been a major economic factor and no estate had ever regarded grouse as anything more than a fringe asset. Consequently, when the crash came there was no urgent economic need to undertake research and management to save Ireland's grouse. Enthusiastic individual proprietors and committed groups of sportsmen like the Northern Ireland Grouse Council and many progressive gun clubs in the Republic of Ireland have continued to struggle to restore grouse on a number of moors. Despite textbook heather-management policies and exemplary predator control there has been only the most minimal recovery on the best moors, and the country-wide situation remains as poor as ever. The factor or, more probably, the combination of factors which caused the collapse of Irish grouse populations in the 1967–73 period remains a mystery. Meanwhile the much-depleted grouse population shows no signs of general recovery. Something is inhibiting Irish grouse recovery and it seems probable that uncontrolled predation, inadequate heather quality and the spread of softwood afforestation are all contributory factors.

Ireland's red grouse are unlikely ever to recover significantly, and it is sad to have to report that their fate seems to be a matter of indifference to all but a relatively small number of enthusiasts. It is interesting, though ultimately fruitless, to speculate what might have been achieved if a stronger pro-grouse lobby had existed in Ireland. Scotland, however is a different matter.

Scotland's grouse enjoy strong and effective support, largely owing to the economic importance of the species. Like its salmon, Scotland's grouse bring large numbers of sportsmen and their families to the country's more remote and least prosperous areas. Free-spending sporting visitors maintain the viability not only of estates but of many hotels and guest-houses, gift shops and service trades of all sorts. The £40 or more per driven brace of grouse shot is only part of the total expenditure of the sportsman who goes grouse shooting in Scotland. His accommodation and other essential requirements involve considerable costs and his wife, family and companions will also contribute to the local economy in a variety of ways. Whole communities benefit as a result – but it is the grouse alone that attract these sportsmen and their friends. If Scotland's grouse decline still further, with falling bags and poorer sport, that income – much of it in valuable foreign currency – will be lost. Estates will make radical changes in their patterns of land use, and the whole upland environment will be irreversibly altered and impoverished in many ways. The future of grouse, in Scotland and throughout upland Britain, involves so much more than just the provision of game shooting. A whole ecological system of great international importance is at stake.

6. The Ptarmigan

Rivalled only by its much larger and rather distant relative the capercaillie, the ptarmigan *(Lagopus mutus)* is by far the most unfamiliar game bird to most sportsmen and ornithologists in Britain. Both these members of the grouse family are now confined to the remoter parts of Scotland. Not only does this place them at a distance from the bulk of the population but the ptarmigan presents us with a further challenge, for it is a bird of the high tops, rarely to be found much below 2,500 feet in the central Highlands. If you drive along the Spey valley or in other Highland areas you might be lucky enough to see a capercaillie from your car, but the ptarmigan demands fitness and stamina on the part of the sportsman if he is to reach its haunts and have the chance of a shot with camera or gun.

This bird is not always a mountain dweller, and on the limits of the British range it can be found as low as 600 feet in the extreme north-west of Scotland. In Scandinavia and

19 *A hen ptarmigan in summer breeding plumage. The camouflage pattern of sandy greys and buffs gives these grouse of the stony high tops protection against predators, as does their all-white winter plumage when the snow comes.*

elsewhere in its circumpolar range it can be found at sea level, for the controlling factor is not altitude but temperature. The ptarmigan is a bird of the coldest and most inhospitable parts of Scotland and for that reason a great many people will never see one, although new opportunities for the armchair ornithologist have been created by the ski-lifts in the Cairngorms, which take the skiers up into the haunts of the ptarmigan. The birds are regularly seen near the ski slopes.

As its Latin name indicates, the ptarmigan is changeable in its appearance, owing to the different plumage patterns it adopts as it moults through the summer and autumn. Like the red grouse, its shooting season comes to an end on 10 December, by which time mature ptarmigan will probably have completed their moult into the pure white winter plumage which is perhaps the most attractive phase of the species. This moult, brought on by a response to a drop in temperature, results in all ptarmigan, of whatever age, turning quite white in mid-winter, apart from the black markings on the tail, which never disappear, and the cock bird's striking black eye-stripe. Males and females both have a red wattle, which is especially prominent when seen against the white winter plumage. Like other grouse species, the cock's wattle is larger.

Camouflage is the justification for this snow-white winter coloration and for the greys and buffs of the summer and autumn phases, for this bird lives in a habitat where its only cover is among boulders and scree and its chief predators are the eagle, the peregrine falcon and, to a lesser extent, the hill fox, the raven, the hoodie crow and the stoat. In spring breeding plumage the cock bird retains the pure white underparts of all ptarmigan but is otherwise coloured a greyish brown barred with white and buff. The breeding female is more generally buff in colour, with a sandy-grey barring and mottling. By autumn both sexes have developed the next phase of their moult, with the male predominantly pale grey and the female a rather greyish sandy brown. From late November to late March the pure white phase gives them the best possible camouflage in a snowy landscape, while their summer and autumn garb allows them to blend with the rocks and lichen-covered stones of the high mountain tops.

The disappearance of the snow in spring is followed by the assumption of individual territories by the males, which display and defend them in a similar way to the more familiar red grouse. The size of the territory is believed to be directly related to the vigour and aggression of the individual male. An ineffectual male who fails to secure an adequate territory may not secure a mate, in which case he may join a summer flock of non-breeding bachelors. Otherwise a monogamous pair-bond is formed and a clutch of between four and eleven eggs will be laid in a shallow scrape. Any available vegetation will be used and the nest will be sparsely lined with heather stalks, hill grasses and feathers. Only in exceptionally good early spring weather will the eggs be laid before mid-May; bad weather may delay egg laying until June. If the first clutch is predated or lost for any reason a late second clutch may even be found in July. The female sits tight and presents a very inconspicuous sight as she incubates her eggs, 25 days being the average incubation period. Like young red grouse and other game bird chicks, young ptarmigan are precocial, on the move and feeding soon after hatching, and they are briefly the joint responsibility of both parent birds before the male disengages from the family group, leaving the female to care for her brood. The young are usually capable of flying for short distances by the time they are 10–14 days old but the brood tends to remain with the hen for a post-hatching period of about twelve weeks, by which time the young are fully grown and the family group is ready to split up.

Because its range is at a higher altitude than the red grouse, the ptarmigan's diet is rather different. Heather remains an important food, however, and is augmented by the berries of bilberry and crowberry and other material such as the buds of birch and willow when these are available. Its diet is much more catholic than that of the red grouse and it will usually feed readily on whatever is available in its sparsely vegetated habitat.

Historically the species has contracted its range in Britain, having died out in Cumbria and the more mountainous parts of Wales towards the end of the eighteenth century. It disappeared from much of southern Scotland and the islands of Mull and Rhum in the 1830s and its retreat into the colder mountain areas of the Highlands may be attributable to a slight tendency towards milder winters in Britain over the period from 1760 onwards. Writers have left us accounts of the Thames and the Cumbrian lakes frozen solid in several winters at that time, and the subsequent milder period would be expected to produce this response in what is essentially a cold-weather species.

Its high-altitude range makes the ptarmigan susceptible to late spring frosts and snow and there can be considerable annual variations in the hatching and survival rate. In bad weather in late spring, chicks are vulnerable to wet and cold, and the availability of food may also be limited by the weather. In addition to these year-to-the-year variations there is some evidence that ptarmigan populations fluctuate in cycles of abundance and scarcity, rather as red grouse do. Why this happens and what the precise nature of the cycles is are questions to be answered by future research, but the Scottish population has been very loosely estimated at between 1,000 and 10,000 pairs. The terrain and altitude of the bird's haunts and the associated weather problems create special difficulties in carrying out an accurate census.

It is probably true to say that fewer sportsmen ever set out to shoot ptarmigan than any other British game species. Not only does the mountain habitat present problems of access for all but the nimble and fit: a long tramp up to the high tops does not guarantee that you will see ptarmigan and, even if you do, their behaviour can be very disconcerting. Freedom from human disturbance makes them naturally very tame and approachable, and they will run for cover or to escape rather than taking to wing with the readiness of red grouse. Most sportsmen are disconcerted by a game bird which behaves like this and, while many enthusiasts would like to be able to record a ptarmigan in their gamebook, few make ptarmigan shooting a regular pursuit. Shooting pressure on the species is so slight as to be negligible and that is unlikely to change in the foreseeable future.

The ptarmigan is something of a trophy for the European sportsman, especially when birds are in the all-white winter plumage. There remains a slight risk of local overshooting in areas where sporting agents or landowners may be tempted to take regular shooting parties, but this is likely to be quite exceptional and of no general significance to the overall population.

The ptarmigan leads its life in areas which remain as yet remote from the polluting and disturbing influence of man and its future therefore seems comparatively secure. But the mountains of Scotland are increasingly the haunt of skiers, rock climbers and ramblers and this facet of the growing leisure use of our countryside must not be overlooked. This disturbance has not so far created problems for the ptarmigan but we must be aware of the possibility of future difficulties.

Meanwhile the ptarmigan remains in its mountain fast-nesses, seen only by a tiny proportion of sportsmen, of whom the majority will be deer stalkers. For them, and for others who may occasionally visit the high tops of our Scottish hills, the ptarmigan will continue to be a welcome sight.

7. The Capercaillie

Everything about the capercaillie is dramatic. There can be no mistaking a capercaillie, for an adult caper, especially a cock bird, is so large and distinctive as to make misidentification impossible. Not only is the capercaillie by far the largest of the grouse family, it is also very much bigger and heavier than any other game bird in the British Isles. The male is a big, bulky, almost black bird with dark-brown wing coverts, a great hooked horn-coloured bill and prominent red wattles over the eyes. 'The size of a turkey' is the Scots countryman's invariable description of a cock capercaillie, and there are certain similarities in the size, posture and sometimes comic vocal accomplishments of these two very distantly related species. The female is barely two-thirds the size of the male, but looks even smaller when the sexes are seen together in the wild. The male's glossy black plumage is missing from the

20 *The cock capercaillie is unmistakeable – a turkey-sized woodland grouse which displays dramatically and noisily in spring. Extinct in Scotland by the 1790s, capercaillie were successfully reintroduced from Sweden in the 1830s. Their survival in Scotland depends on suitable habitat, especially mature Scots pines.*

female, which has a predominantly rufous and greyish-brown plumage – a duller and more subtle pattern of barred and mottled buffs, browns and russets by comparison with the strikingly bold coloration of the very much bigger and more conspicuous male.

Boldness is apparent not only in the colour, size and posture of the cock capercaillie, but also in his aggressive behaviour, especially in spring. Studies of breeding capercaillie in Scotland, Germany and Scandinavia all tend to confirm that an ability to display aggressively and to fight off other males can give a mature male caper such a dominant position that he will be able to mate with perhaps 70 per cent or more of the attendant harem of hens. These particularly prominent, or 'alpha', individuals seem to enjoy a form of *droit de seigneur* over most of the local females, with 'beta' or subdominant males attaining a much smaller proportion of matings, and the remaining cock birds achieving very few matings and these only when opportunity arises.

The breeding behaviour of capercaillie is similar in certain respects to that of its close relative the black grouse, but there are important differences too. It is probably wise not to call the communal display of the capercaillie a 'lek', since that term is better reserved for the very clearly defined and age-old open-country displaying grounds of blackcock. While blackcocks lek in an open space, the display areas of capercaillie are generally right inside the forest, often in and around a group of mature trees. Depending upon the weather, the first signs of breeding activity and territorial display can be seen as early as February, or even exceptionally in January; the peak period for mating and egg laying is from mid-April to mid-May.

Cock capers begin their displays by calling loudly from their tree-top roosting perches, and this song often begins some hours before dawn. With the coming of daylight the birds fly down to the forest floor and the male's territorial song is then supplemented by a prominent physical display as this impressively large bird struts and paces about. This activity takes place to the accompaniment of a bizarre range of vocal sounds, including clicks, scraping and rattling sounds, belchings, clonkings, something very reminiscent of a turkey gobble, and, strangest of all, a resonant 'pop' like a tight cork being drawn from a bottle.

This vocal virtuosity is paralleled by a wide range of physical movements and postures, the most dramatic of which are the peacock-like fanning of the erect tail feathers and an upward stretch of the neck which thrusts out the 'beard', a patch of feathers below the lower mandible and on the throat. Recent studies seem to indicate that all this swagger and bluster is intended not so much as an attraction to hen birds as a statement of a territorial claim and an act of

21 *A hen capercaillie on her nest. She is much smaller than the male and incubates alone, her clutch averaging eight eggs.*

defiance and belligerent intimidation towards other males. The aggressive posturing of these cock birds frequently leads to a direct physical clash in which thrashing wings and those prominent and powerful bills are the principal weapons. Immediate fatalities seem to be extremely rare but there is a high incidence of wounding and a significant number of cock birds will die later from injuries received in these territorial battles. The aggression of cock capers in spring is extreme, and some birds will not hesitate to attack dogs and even humans. Many a shepherd or forester has been glad of a crook or stout stick with which to fend off the approaches of an angry cock caper defending his territory.

The most aggressive and powerful cocks achieve a dominance which is rewarded by their mating with the majority of hen birds, and the promiscuity of these 'alpha' birds is particularly evident from the rapid sequence of matings with a number of hens which follows their assertion of dominance during the display. There is no permanent bond between male and female but only the most fleeting of temporary pairings at the time of mating, after which the female lays her single clutch of eggs, which, like the black grouse, averages eight in number, and incubates, broods and rears the chicks on her own. Like many game birds, capercaillie chicks are active within hours of hatching and the brood will be on the move within a day or so after the last egg hatches, following an incubation period of about 26 days.

The capercaillie is, throughout most of its range, a resident of old-established pine woods, principally Scots pine, or a mixture of pine forest and deciduous woodland. We know it to be indigenous to Britain, for archaeological evidence points to its presence in very ancient times. Its eventual decline and final extinction in the wild in the British Isles was due solely to the destruction of the habitat essential to its survival, and the story of its reintroduction and the subsequent success of its spread and recolonisation is a significant and encouraging one, and worth recounting in some detail.

Although the historical record is not quite precise, it seems clear that the last native capercaillie in Scotland became extinct towards the end of the eighteenth century, while the last birds in Ireland disappeared around 1790. Little more than a generation later came the successful moves to reintroduce this species, pioneered by Sir Thomas Fowell Buxton, Lord Breadalbane and others in the 1830s. This represents one of the most notable and successful examples of a reintroduction by nineteenth-century enthusiasts, many of whom made attempts – individually, and collectively as acclimatisation societies – to establish lost or alien species in Britain.

The immediate inspiration behind this introduction seems to have come from Llewellyn Lloyd, a Welsh Quaker, keen sportsman and prolific writer who lived in Sweden in the early nineteenth century. Lloyd made a study of capercaillie in Scandinavia, where they remained relatively common, and took the view that Scotland still had sufficient residual areas of its once-extensive Scots pine forests together with other areas of newer coniferous woodland created by some fairly widespread afforestation programmes by Highland proprietors, especially in what are now the Grampian and Tayside regions. Sir Thomas Fowell Buxton of Cromer in Norfolk, a keen sportsman, friend of Llewellyn Lloyd and incidentally a close parliamentary colleague of William Wilberforce in the campaign to abolish slavery, became a driving force behind the capercaillie reintroduction project. After inspecting a number of Highland estates for their suitability as release points for imported birds he eventually reached an agreement with his friend and shooting companion Lord Breadalbane, whose estate at Taymouth Castle in east Perthshire appeared to be particularly suitable. Buxton was especially familiar with the Taymouth property, having shot there as Lord Breadalbane's guest, and he had ample opportunity fully to assess the nature of the ground and the suitability of the habitat.

Llewellyn Loyd set about co-ordinating the catching up of Swedish capercaillie to be sent to Scotland, advertising widely in country areas known to sustain good populations of caper, and offering a generous bounty to any country people who could supply him with suitable birds in a fit and undamaged state. His requests were even read to rural congregations from the pulpits of churches in suitable parts of Sweden. He advocated the use of a snare or 'springe', modified so as to catch but not to kill the birds by having a 'stop' or knot to prevent the noose from closing too tightly.

In an age when we take for granted the easy and speedy intercontinental movement of people and animals by air it is difficult for us to appreciate all the difficulties and hardship involved in bringing 29 adult capercaillie – 13 cocks and 16 hens – overland across Scandinavia by farm cart and then from Sweden by mail steamer and on horse-drawn waggons. All the organisation of this tough and logistically complicated transport operation was entrusted to Lawrence Banville,

Buxton's Irish gamekeeper. His diaries and other contemporary evidence show him to have been a real enthusiast, thoroughly committed to the project in hand and gifted with the aviculturist's equivalent of green fingers. He already had some experience of looking after a captive pair of capercaillie which had been sent to Cromer some years previously, and these had duly laid and hatched a clutch of eggs. Although the hen bird and her brood did not survive for long, Larry Banville had acquired vitally important experience in caring for caper in captivity before he set off to join Llewellyn Lloyd in Sweden in the spring of 1837. His journey marked the beginning of an eminently successful project, despite the fact that it began on the unpropitious date of 1 April.

By early May thirty capercaillie had already been collected at Lloyd's house at Venusburg, and more birds came in almost daily. The extremely aggressive attitude of all adult grouse, especially cock birds, always poses problems when they are kept in close proximity in captivity, and Banville had to pen his cock capers singly after several deaths as the result of furious fights. To add to his trials he also had to guard his charges from the disturbing attentions of crowds of visitors who came, especially on Sundays, to see the captive birds and to listen to the cock birds' extensive and extraordinary-sounding spring vocal repertoire. Larry Banville's devotion to his birds and dedication to the reintroduction project was eventually rewarded by his safe arrival with his consignment of birds at Taymouth Castle late on Saturday 24 June 1837.

Buxton's notes record that by the summer of 1838 a total of 13 cock capercaillie and 29 hen birds had been delivered to Lord Breadalbane. Evidently the birds had settled well and produced a worthwhile crop of eggs, for the head keeper, Mr Guthrie, felt it unnecessary to undertake the labour-intensive and time-consuming business of hatching and rearing all his young caper in captivity. Instead, many of the eggs laid by the captive capercaillie hens were taken out and placed in the nests of wild blackgame. This gamble paid off handsomely, with at least 49 capercaillie successfully hatched and reared by grey hens at Taymouth Castle in 1839. A smaller number were reared and released, and by mid-September a total of between 60 and 70 young capercaillie were at large in the Taymouth Castle preserves.

The consolidation and firm establishment of this introduced population was helped by a low level of disturbance and a total ban by Lord Breadalbane on the shooting not only of capercaillie but also of blackgame, in case a young caper should be mistaken for a black grouse. Most important was that the reintroduction took full account of the bird's basic environmental requirements, and the greatest care was taken to ensure that the species was not merely left to take its chance in an unsuitable or hostile habitat. This is in marked contrast to some of the 'chuck and chance it' releases and introductions attempted by other Victorian 'acclimatisers', whose activities were often characterised more by enthusiasm than by ecological understanding.

By the summer of 1842, five years after the arrival of the Swedish birds at Taymouth Castle, Lord Breadalbane was sufficiently satisfied by the success of the project to feel able to relax his ban on shooting. In October 1841 he had written to Buxton to report that 'the Capercaili had striven most excellently. The experiment of putting the eggs under the grey hen was attended with perfect success and there are now a goodly number of these birds hereabout.' By the next summer he evidently felt that a small shootable surplus existed and so a very select group of guns was duly assembled. Most appropriately, Sir Thomas Fowell Buxton was one of two guests on that first shooting day, 8 September 1842, the other gun being Prince Albert, the Prince Consort, who was holidaying in the Highlands with Queen Victoria. Despite the 'cocks only' instructions of the host, the day's bag is reported to have contained only one capercaillie, and a hen at that! History does not relate which gun accounted for this bird, a runner which was eventually picked and shown at the end of the day to the admiring Queen, who recorded it in her Highland journal as 'a magnificent bird'. Could it have fallen to Prince Albert's gun?

The success of that first Taymouth Castle capercaillie

reintroduction was sustained over the decades which followed, and by the early 1870s Lord Breadalbane's head keeper estimated the stock of caper of the estate at about two thousand birds. Lord Breadalbane claimed the more cautiously conservative figure of one thousand, but there can be no doubt that a flourishing and expanding population of capercaillie had become established within thirty years of Larry Banville's first arrival at Taymouth with his precious consignment of Swedish captives.

The spread of capercaillie in Scotland in the latter part of the nineteenth century resulted from the expansion of this firmly established colony. The Tay valley with its extensive plantations was soon well populated with caper and the species expanded its geographical range by colonising every suitable wooded valley and glen in Perthshire, with some tendency also for the birds to move north-eastwards into Kincardineshire and Angus. By the early 1900s capercaillie were well established across most of the eastern central Highlands, with substantial populations present up to the Golspie area of south-east Sutherland and as far away as Loch Lomond and Argyllshire in the south-west.

The success of Buxton and Breadalbane's reintroduction in Perthshire caught the imagination of other Victorian enthusiasts and a number of badly planned, half-hearted or otherwise ill conceived attempts were made to introduce capercaillie in various parts of northern England, the West Country, Wales and Ireland. In almost every instance the failure of these projects can be attributed to the unsuitability of the habitat and to the acclimatisers' ignorance of the basic requirements of the species.

Ireland, for example, had once sustained a widespread and thriving population of capercaillie, which was commented upon by the early travellers and topographers. Giraldus of Wales, writing about 1185, mentioned the Irish woods and their abundance of wild peacocks', a name derived from the cock capercaillie's spectacular fantail display. But changes in land use and the growing fuel demands of a rapidly expanding population made constant inroads into the once extensive

Irish forests of Scots pine and oak. This process was made worse by the effects of the repeated wars and insurrections of the Elizabethan and Jacobean periods, which led to further extensive burning and felling of old native forests as successive English expeditionary forces sought to flush out elusive bands of Irish guerrillas or 'woodkernes' and destroy their woodland hiding places. By the 1650s several centuries of this civil and military attrition had resulted in the almost total disappearance of Ireland's ancient woodlands and Oliver Cromwell's surveyors reported that the capercaillie population had declined seriously. By the 1750s only a small relict population remained in the south-west of Munster and the last native Irish capercaillie finally disappeared about 1790.

When Victorian enthusiasts like Colonel Cooper of Markree Castle in County Sligo made their attempts to reintroduce the capercaillie to Ireland the imported birds were released into a countryside where the habitat was totally inappropriate, if not downright hostile to them. Lack of food, excessive predation and the activities of poachers all combined to defeat the handful of nineteenth-century Irish introductions. The only capercaillie in Ireland today are to be seen as mounted specimens in vast glass cabinets in a few country houses, dramatic and melancholy reminders of the well intentioned but ultimately inept attempts of our ancestors.

In Scotland today the capercaillie is well established throughout Easter Ross, the Grampian and Tayside regions, and across the southern Highlands to Loch Lomondside and into Argyllshire. Any future expansion in its range, and indeed its continuance in its present haunts, is almost entirely a question of habitat. Overshooting could perhaps be an inhibiting factor but the majority of sporting proprietors now operate sensible shooting regimes which remove only a shootable surplus and avoid making damaging inroads into breeding stock. This desirable attitude is helped by a healthy dose of enlightened self-interest too. The sporting value of capercaillie, especially when one is dealing with European visitors, for whom mature cock capercaillies are highly prized trophies, can be very substantial indeed, and there are clear economic advantages in maintaining a flourishing population.

The forests, their trees, the various species, age distribution and the attendant undergrowth in and around the forest are the true keys to the future well-being of our capercaillie populations. The decided habitat preference is for mature conifers, especially Scots pines, growing in an open pattern with an undergrowth of heather, blaeberry and other plants characteristic of the fringe of the moor. The recent and still current practice of planting large areas with a monoculture of even-aged exotic softwoods like Sitka spruce is distinctly unfavourable to capercaillie, especially where these new conifer blocks are so planted as to leave few open spaces to promote a varied undergrowth of budding and fruiting vegetation.

Recent research both in Scotland and in Europe has shown the importance to capercaillie of single, old, well established Scots pines, now generally referred to as 'grannies'. The presence or absence of these mature trees can have a far-reaching impact on the capercaillie population, and extensive clear-felling and replanting with new and unimaginatively planned blocks of even-aged softwoods will result in a dramatic fall in capercaillie numbers. Despite the ill considered layout of much modern afforestation, nature and natural forces occasionally take a hand. Fire can burn out an area which will subsequently be replanted, thereby creating a desirable 'edge' effect and a variety of tree ages, while high winds cause windthrow damage which may also produce much the same result. If the felling of areas of mature, harvestable conifers is intelligently co-ordinated, many of our softwood forests may in time become infinitely more attractive to wildlife of many species, and to capercaillie in particular. But with this species, as with so many others, the future will probably be dictated by the harsh realities of forestry economics and the soulless exigencies of the accountants' balance sheets. The case of the capercaillie is just one component in the wider argument for a more integrated approach to land use, whereby crops such as softwood timber can go hand in hand with a rich and diverse flora and fauna. Far from constituting a threat to the profitability of softwood afforestation as a form of upland land use, the intelligent and imaginative design and management of conifer forests can not only represent a viable form of land use in the uplands but can help produce a landscape which has enormous value in ecological, aesthetic and recreational terms. How does one put a price on that?

8. The Black Grouse

Like its cousin the capercaillie, the black grouse (*Tetrao tetrix*) is a bird of woodlands, but this smaller bird shows a more marked preference for the edges of the forest. Its favourite habitat is the transitional areas where trees give way to open moorland, heath, bogs or marginal farming areas. In the birds' general biology, breeding habits and some aspects of the courtship display there are many similarities with the capercaillie, but the most striking and obvious difference between them is in size. A full-grown male capercaillie is a monster among game birds, which will weigh at least 9 pounds or more, while a mature blackcock will average around 3¼ pounds. Despite their discrepancy in size these species have a great deal in common, more than any two other British game birds. Sadly, while the capercaillie has come back from extinction to its current well established status in Scotland, thanks to reintroduction and subsequent natural spread, the black grouse has been in serious decline in Britain for more than a century. This is just one facet of a much greater international crisis for the species, which is now under very serious threat of extinction in many parts of its range, which stretches through Scandinavia, northern and central Europe and right across Asia to eastern Mongolia.

Its British decline has been rapid and dramatic, and we often forget how relatively widespread and common this species used to be. When the surveyors acting for the National Rifle Association went to examine Bagshot Heath in Surrey in the 1880s with a view to transferring the NRA's ranges from Wimbledon to Bisley, they found that black grouse (or blackgame) were plentiful on the Surrey heathland with its natural vegetation of heather and Scots pine. A thorough survey published in 1924 reported that there were only six counties in England and Wales where black grouse had never been recorded. They used to be common in early Victorian times in Hampshire, especially in the New Forest, Wiltshire and Dorset and almost everywhere south of the Thames, and were well established throughout the West Country. Wales, especially the northern counties, formerly held good numbers, and so too did the north Midlands. The British record bag is held by Cannock Chase in Staffordshire, where 252 head were shot in one day's driven blackgame shooting in 1860. Bag sizes are, in broad terms, a reliable indicator of the relative abundance of a species, and clearly the moorland fringes of Cannock Chase sustained a flourishing black grouse population at that period. About the same time Lord Berkeley Paget made a bag of 126 blackgame to his own gun in a single day in the Cannock area. So widespread and locally numerous were black grouse that a late Victorian writer stated that they had been 'shot in every county from Caithness to Cornwall.'

Today there are remnant populations in parts of the West Country, Derbyshire, north Wales and Cumbria, but Scotland is now the only area of Britain where blackgame are at all numerous. As with our wild game fish – resident brown trout and migratory salmon and sea trout – Scotland is the last stronghold and the natural focus for research to help promote

22 *The black cock indulges in very animated dawn and dusk displays, when numbers of males congregate on communal lekking grounds. The large red eye wattles, the lyre-shaped tail and the white under-tail feathers all play a prominent part in this sexual display.*

---

the future of the species in Britain. Elsewhere in Europe and Asia, only Scandinavia and Russia still have black grouse in any real numbers, a sad reflection on a bird which was formerly Europe's commonest grouse species everywhere north of the Alps. Two of the most dramatic statistics come from Holland and Denmark. Dutch biologists witnessed a population crash of around 93 per cent over a thirty-year period from 1950 to 1980 on one study area, while Jutland's black grouse have declined from an already depleted population of just over a thousand birds in the mid-1960s to virtual extinction today.

The size and extent of the problem is very serious and is engaging the urgent attention of biologists and sportsmen everywhere. In Scotland a joint research project is being carried out by the Institute of Terrestrial Ecology and the World Pheasant Association.

All kinds of questions need to be answered before we know how best to take steps to help the species. Are black grouse subject to cycles of abundance and scarcity, and if so why? Can management help to iron out these fluctuations? What can be done to ensure that adequate habitat and a suitable environment remains available for them? Can research provide the answers and develop practical management strategies, or will the decline continue, as has happened in so many areas with the grey partridge?

Black grouse, especially males, are unmistakable. Even more than capercaillie, the adult male's plumage is almost black, relieved only by a white bar on the wing and a flash of white on the wrist joint. The covert feathers beneath the tail are also white, and these are prominent in the male's spring lek displays. There is a prominent blood-red wattle over each eye, and this becomes raised and enlarged as part of the territorial and sexual display. Most distinctive of all is the superb forked, almost lyre-shaped tail which is the black-cock's trophy – worn proudly in the bonnets of bandsmen in Scottish regiments and in the hats of European sportsmen. The European tradition is to stalk and shoot the adult male on his displaying grounds in early spring, in much the same way that capercaillie are traditionally shot and at a time of year when both birds enjoy breeding-season protection in Britain. If that lyre-shaped tail is the desired souvenir of a day after blackgame then it is well to wait until some weeks after the opening of the British shooting season on 20 August. Not until later in the autumn will the males have moulted fully and completed the development of the characteristically shaped tail.

By that date the smaller, brownish hen with her black-barred and speckled plumage will have reared her brood of young to a shootable size, but the juveniles will still be noticeably smaller than their parents, and a covey coming forward on a driven grouse shoot may be mistaken for red grouse. Black grouse are notoriously difficult to drive with any degree of accuracy and do not lend themselves to the regimented driving days which are commonplace with red grouse. On the wing blackgame have a typical grouse-like flight, rapid wingbeats alternating with fast gliding. The difference in size is most apparent when red and black grouse are seen in the air together, and the black grouse's larger and bulkier build is very apparent. Its flight is fast, deceptively so and noticeably quicker than a red grouse. This was first brought home to me by something I saw when training a young setter on a Galloway moor in early September. A single adult red grouse was pointed and flushed, flying fast across a wide valley. A solitary blackcock had been lying only yards from the red grouse, among some dwarf willow. He too was flushed a few seconds afterwards and flew off in the same direction, gaining rapidly and eventually overtaking the red grouse towards the far side of the glen. His strength and speed of flight was all the more remarkable as he was clearly still in the moult and lacked the fully developed forked tail and the finished plumage of a blackcock in winter. In late summer the males tend to become solitary and secretive as they moult, living quite separate from the hens and their broods. At times they can often be found only by using pointers or setters, as they squat tight in dense grasses and other low cover, reluctant to fly and with much impaired powers of flight.

The spring sexual displays and mating of black grouse are particularly interesting and dramatic. They will probably begin in late March or early April, and before this the males in particular may have been living a communal life in packs or even large flocks. These seem to form during the worst winter weather of January and February, and there are eyewitness accounts of flocks of more than a hundred birds having been seen in severe weather in Britain. The same phenomenon is more regularly reported from parts of northern Europe and western Asia, where winter weather is much more severe.

Males continue in groups, each of which has a collective home range. Within that area each individual takes his place within a hierarchy and will have a territory which he will assert and defend against other males. Display and mating, however, is a group affair, and takes place on areas of ground to which the birds return each spring, sometimes for generations or even centuries. Some leks are deserted after a few years for no apparent reason, while others continue, seemingly unaffected by even quite extreme forms of human disturbance such as forestry clear-felling and the building of new trunk roads. Displaying males congregate at the lekking arenas in the mornings in autumn, but at both dawn and dusk in spring. The lek is invariably an area of short vegetation surrounded by longer growth where the birds can feed, find cover and nest. Forest clearings, open patches of pasture or other grassland, and flat areas of heather-covered bog are often chosen. In Scandinavia leks may even be on the ice of small frozen lakes. The essential requirements seem to be openness combined with relative proximity to the woodland edge and the cover and security it affords.

The numbers of cock birds at leks varies, with some astonishing Russian reports of up to 200 present, but these are quite an exception. Between eight and ten cocks is the average, and the intensity of their displaying increases as the days lengthen and the females gravitate towards the periphery of the lek. The actual lekking display is a combination of physical posturing, movement and calling. An individual's display may begin with a series of hissing or sneezing noises accompanied by a jumping and fluttering, leading to the physical posture typical of the lekking male. The head is held high and stiffly, wings droop outwards in a loose half-mast attitude and the tail is fully fanned to reveal the prominent black feathers and also the startlingly white under-tail covert feathers which are fluffed out in a bouquet. The appearance of one or more hen birds or the arrival of an additional male around the lek further intensifies the level of flutter-jumping until all the participants are assembled. Pairs of males confront each other in aggressive defence of their territories. Those red wattles are now at their most prominent and distended, the neck is swollen and the chin feathers stick out. Heads bob up and down stiffly and animatedly and the cocks lean forward, wings hanging and revealing the white shoulder patches, and with tail feathers fully extended and arching outwards, surmounted by the white of the under-tail feathers.

The characteristic call at this stage is often referred to as *roo-koo*ing, a surprisingly soft and almost dovelike call which seems to go on for a long time without a pause for breath. The cocks make short dashes at each other, and wings and bills may be used in a combat which often results in the breaking of primary feathers. But the fights seem rarely to involve the use of the birds' feet and are largely confined to wing-clashing and pecking at an opponent's neck or head.

The lek seems to fulfil many purposes. It provides the males with a means of establishing and maintaining a hierarchy and a system of territories; it advertises to the hens the whereabouts of the cock birds; and it is believed also to stimulate the sexual receptivity of the females. When a female enters a male's territory and assumes a squatting posture it is the signal for mating, which may not take place instantly as the male continues to circle around the squatting female. After the fleeting seconds of actual mating the female usually runs or flies off without delay, and observers have noted that most females will have mated within fifteen or twenty minutes of their arrival at the lek.

After mating the females are left on their own to lay and hatch their eggs and raise their young, the promiscuous males having no more interest in the matter. A fertilised female will choose her nesting site, a simple scrape in the ground, well concealed in long grasses, heather or low scrub. Occasional tree nests have been recorded, invariably the abandoned old nest of another species. The full clutch of eggs numbers seven or eight, similar to the capercaillie, and the hen rears only one brood. Like other species of single-brooded game birds, however, she may lay a second clutch if the first is destroyed or predated. The clutch should be complete after about twelve days following the laying of the first egg and the incubation period of 24–27 days begins with the laying of the final eggs.

Like most game birds, blackgame chicks are active within hours of hatching and will move about and feed vigorously in the vicinity of the nest, tended by the hen. Scientists are studying the breeding biology of blackgame using much the same techniques as for red grouse, partridge and pheasant, with radio-tagging as one of their principal aids. Grey hens caught at the lek – the only time and place where this can be done efficiently – are fitted with radio transmitters which enable the subsequent fate of the hen and later her brood to be followed in some detail. Pinpointing the overnight roosting site is particularly useful since the droppings of both the chicks and their mother can be collected for analysis to show what they have been eating. In spring and early summer the hen bird lives almost entirely on a vegetarian diet. Leaves, seeds, berries and flowers make up her principal fare, in contrast to her chicks, which will be gobbling up insects as a very major part of their food intake. By sweeping with a net or using some similar form of sampling biologists can easily find out what species of insects are present in an area, and their relative abundance, and this can be compared with the tiny fragments of insects detected in the chicks' droppings. The result shows which insects are prefered by the chicks, and the growth rate and survival success of different broods can be linked with the availability of insects in their feeding areas. Already the Scottish-based research work has shown that blackgame chicks survive better where insect food is readily available to them.

About three weeks after hatching the young birds are able to fly short distances but these cheepers are not really well developed and strong on the wing before late August, and the males do not assume their splendid adult plumage until much later still. The slower rate at which black grouse mature, compared with the smaller red grouse, is given some acknowledgement by the law, which only permits the shooting of blackgame from 20 August – a token eight days later than red grouse and ptarmigan. In fact it will be unusual to find a covey of blackgame which are really forward, sporting birds until September, and in general the birds, both well grown

23 *Spot the grey hen? The pointer has located a well camouflaged hen bird with her covey of well grown chicks in long heather on the fringes of a Berwickshire grouse moor. Black grouse will often sit very tight and can be difficult to find in late summer.*

juveniles and post-moulting adults, are at their best in October and November.

As has been mentioned, blackgame are difficult to drive to standing guns and they occupy a fringe position in most sportsmen's scheme of things. If a covey or two comes over the butts there may be a black grouse or two in the bag after a day's grouse driving, and they have rarely tended to be anything other than an occasional 'various' in most game-books. Few guns ever set out with blackgame as their principal quarry, but there are some enthusiasts who achieve modest bags of a few brace by dogging with setters and pointers in those areas on the fringes of the moors where blackgame are most likely to be found. This is in keeping with the European tradition of shooting game *devant soi* or *au chien d'arrêt* rather than *en battue*, and it can allow experienced guns to shoot very selectively by identifying old birds from young, and adult males from females. There is some disagreement about what selective shooting approach is best, or if it matters at all. Traditionally, grey hens are not shot, but it is argued that older, barren females may disrupt young breeding hens at nesting time and should therefore be shot in preference to young birds. Equally it is urged that the juveniles provide the harvestable surplus which, if not shot, will fall victims to predation, disease, the weather and other natural factors. Perhaps it does not really matter: a no-hens policy seems not to result in any increase in blackgame numbers.

Shooting pressure on black grouse is low largely because the species does not conveniently fit into the traditional British pattern, and the decline of the species in so many areas cannot be accounted for by overshooting. Loss of suitable habitat seems, once again, to be the chief culprit and as a species black grouse seem to be particularly susceptible to environmental and ecological changes. Those birds which succeed in taking up residence in areas which provide the habitat to which the species is best adapted will inevitably have a better chance of survival and breeding success than others in less favourable, marginal areas. If a species is slow to adapt and has very precise requirements in terms of its ecological niche, it naturally suffers as changing land uses modify the habitat. Perhaps this, in brief, is the key to the widespread decline of black grouse world-wide. Across most of its former range human pressures have altered the face of the landscape. Radical changes in farming, forestry, levels of human disturbance and environmental pollution may have combined to erode the critical niche in which blackgame once flourished so abundantly.

To look on the brighter side, there are some hopeful signs for black grouse in certain parts of the British Isles, especially in Scotland. Large-scale afforestation with conifers seems to have helped re-establish blackgame in areas where they had been absent for decades, and in this respect afforestation has probably benefited both blackgame and its close relative the capercaillie. But large, even-aged monocultures of blanket forestry are far from ideal, and much may be achieved for these woodland grouse, and for many other forms of wildlife too, if the forests of the future are designed and planted more creatively and with more concern for game and other species. Small numbers of birch, rowan and other upland species of tree can break up the monotony of endless stands of spruce, with minimal effects on the timber crop but very beneficial results for birds, deer, small mammals and plants. Unplanted stream-sides, small unplanted clearings and more 'edge effect' – whether created by different species, tree ages, clear-felling, or by accidents like windthrow or fire – will all help to make the commercial softwood production much more attractive to a great variety of wildlife, including blackgame.

These are some general principles, but the continuing research on black grouse may help develop some specific management strategies to promote the species. Concern is growing for its future well-being and there are moves afoot to attempt to establish blackgame in Ireland, now a well afforested country compared with what it was even as recently as a generation ago. Plans for such an introduction, and the enthusiasm and dedication of those who are striving to ensure its success, are yet another hopeful sign for blackgame. If they do eventually flourish in well managed areas of forestry it will not only be a wonderful reversal of the fortunes of the species; it will also atone in some measure for the damage which uninformed and thoughtless afforestation has wrought among our game and wildlife in so many upland areas. It will be a significant step towards better land use – with agriculture, silviculture, game and other wildlife co-existing in a harmonious and greatly enriched environment. Profitable crops, of timber or anything else, are not necessarily incompatible with abundant flora and fauna, better recreational and amenity opportunities and a secure future for game and field sports.

9. The Snipe

Since 1981, when its diminutive and rather distant cousin the jack snipe (*Lymnocryptes minimus*) was given total protection in Great Britain by the Wildlife and Countryside Act, the common snipe (*Gallinago gallinago*) has become quite the smallest game bird which the British sportsman will encounter. Yet its sporting qualities and the high regard in which it is held throughout its almost world-wide range are out of all proportion to the snipe's small size.

It is quite unmistakable – a slender, racy bird, easily identified by its long bill, pointed wings, and characteristic *scaape-scaape* cry when it is flushed. It springs quickly when disturbed and its fast and erratic zigzag flight makes it a testing shot for the sportsman. No other game bird is so consistently difficult to hit when guns are walking up, while a driven snipe presents a very different but equally challenging target as it zips fast and low across a marsh, or comes forward high on flickering sickle-shaped wings with a faltering, almost hovering flight which makes its true speed and distance so very difficult to judge accurately. When we add to this its delicious plump-fleshed qualities at the table we have, all in all, a very desirable quarry species indeed.

Like its relative the woodcock, the snipe occupies something of a grey area in terms of the laws on game. Neither species is game within the strict legal meaning of that term, and in Great Britain the open season for shooting and close season protection is not a matter for the game laws but is dealt with by the Wildlife and Countryside Act 1981. Although in this respect snipe and woodcock are regarded as wildfowl, a game licence is nevertheless necessary if you wish to shoot either species. So, for all practical purposes, the sportsman must regard woodcock and snipe in the same light as other game species. This is perhaps further evidence that the law is an ass, or at any rate that the game laws are rather less than straightforward!

The snipe is a relatively common resident bird in Britain and Ireland, and has been recorded as breeding in every county. This pattern of breeding distribution in the British Isles is only a local reflection of its thoroughly widespread global distribution. Various subspecies of the common snipe and other separate but closely related species are found throughout the Northern Hemisphere and in all continents wherever the habitat is suitable. Habitat is a critical factor in determining the distribution of this rather specialised little bird. It is technically classified as a wader, a marshland bird adapted to wet feeding grounds in which it seeks its food by probing in mud and ooze with that slender bill which averages 2¾ inches long, over a quarter of the bird's entire body length. This is a precision instrument, long and smooth,

24 *The snipe is our smallest game bird and is well adapted to feeding by wading in shallow water and probing in mud and ooze with its long, sensitive bill.*

and with the upper mandible fractionally longer than the lower. The bill ends in a slightly bulbous enlargement, with the extreme tip being rather harder than the rest of the otherwise pliable and sensitive bill end. This enables the snipe to search for and identify its food by touch rather than by sight. Dissection and microscopic examination of the bill has revealed a structure of hexagonally shaped cells, rather like a honeycomb pattern, and this sophisticated sensory system lets the snipe feed precisely and efficiently in the top layers of soft ground to a depth of about 2 inches. Once food has been located the snipe can flex its upper mandible to grip and extract items of food without having to open its entire bill.

The snipe's eyes are relatively unimportant in its search for food and they are set further back in the head than is the case with most other waders and shore birds. Only the woodcock has its eyes set further back, and like its bigger cousin the snipe enjoys excellent vision to the sides and to the rear. Both woodcock and snipe can actually see directly behind them, and this has an obvious survival value in helping them avoid predators while spending much of their time in a head-down feeding position. Important protection and concealment also comes from the highly effective natural camouflage of the snipe's plumage. The colouring is a disrupted pattern of black, browns, creams and buffs, which makes it a rare event to see the bird on the ground without resorting to a hide and waiting for snipe to feed into the range of your binoculars or camera lens. On shooting days the first sight of a snipe will invariably be a flicker of the wings as it springs into the wind, followed by a flash of white from the pale feathers of the belly and the underside of the wings as its turns and jinks away.

Anyone who has shot snipe regularly will know well how effective that camouflage can be, even when a snipe has been shot and its fall has been marked accurately on the short, almost bare herbage of a bog or marsh. If the bird falls with only its back and upper wing feathers exposed it may take a good bit of finding, but a bird lying on its back will stand out clearly like a large white pebble owing to the startling whiteness of the belly feathers and underparts. A gun walking up without a dog who is lucky enough to shoot a right-and-left at snipe may have a very real problem ahead of him. Perhaps the best method, as advocated by the late Lord Dunsany, who was not only an eminent playwright and novelist but a supremely accomplished shot and above all a connoisseur of snipe shooting, is to drop a handkerchief or other marker on the spot where you were standing when the shots were fired. This at least gives you a starting point from which to try to locate your two birds, by walking in turn to the point where the fall of each bird was marked. But a steady retriever with a good nose, walking quietly to heel, is really essential if lost birds and wasted time are to be avoided when walking up snipe, since the bird's plumage is so well adapted to the colours of its typical shooting-season habitat of bogs and marshes, where dead grasses, rushes and heather predominate.

The harsh *scaape* alarm call of the snipe is characteristic of our autumn and winter encounters with this species, but spring and the onset of the breeding season are marked by a quite different sound, which has given rise to many of the local and vernacular names for the snipe. At dawn and dusk and on into the hours of darkness a reedy bleating sound like that of a goat can be heard as breeding snipe indulge in their mating flights. This has given rise to age-old names for the snipe in Welsh, Scots and Irish gaelic with meanings like 'goat of the air', 'goat of the bogs', 'goat of the night', 'heather bleater', 'bog bleater', and many more. Similar names are to be found around the Baltic and in other European areas where breeding snipe are common, but other Continental names tend to concentrate on the snipe's most prominent feature, its long bill — hence, for example, the French *bécassine*, from the word *bec*, meaning beak or bill.

The strange and unmistakable throbbing vibrato sound made by snipe in the breeding season is variously called 'bleating', 'drumming' or 'winnowing', and for a long time it was a puzzle to naturalists and sportsmen. Some thought that it was vocal while others maintained that it was caused by the bird's wings; all were intrigued by this mysterious, almost eerie sound made by displaying birds in a dipping, diving flight. Our understanding of this noise progressed when, in the 1850s, Dr W. Meves experimented by fixing a snipe's tail feathers to a long stick. When this was swung through the air he claimed that the vibrating feathers produced the bleating note. A more elaborate experiment by the German naturalist Rohweder involved having a taxidermist mount a complete specimen of a snipe in a diving posture. When air was blown fast over the tail feathers Rohweder too claimed that the bleating or drumming note was heard. The question was finally answered thanks largely to the work of Sir Philip Manson-Bahr, who made a careful study at Cambridge in 1907 of snipe tail feathers, following field observations that a diving, drumming snipe extends its two outer tail feathers at a greater angle than the others. It is now known that bleating results from the vibrations of these two outer tail feathers when the snipe dives at an air speed of 25 m.p.h. or more. The pitch of the sound varies with the bird's speed but a typical bleat results from an air speed of around 40 m.p.h. An interesting practical demonstration was given in the 1920s by Eric Parker, then editor of *The Field*. He carefully fixed a snipe's tail feathers to an arrow, with the outer feathers set at an extended angle. The arrow was shot at an acute angle into the air and on its descent a drumming sound could clearly be heard.

One of the many remarkable aspects of this drumming or bleating noise is the distance the sound will carry. This can be over half a mile in still air, and even further in ideal conditions when the sound is carried on the breeze. A bleat will usually last for two or three seconds and on warm, still nights with a bright moon it may go on intermittently all through the night, usually reaching its peak around dusk and dawn. It is a sexual display by the male snipe over his breeding territory and seems to play a part in the pairing up of breeding birds, in defining the nesting area and in staking a claim against other male intruders during the period of mating and incubation. Female snipe can and do bleat, but patient and careful observation by scientists has shown that it is overwhelmingly a male activity. At all events it is a distinct and unmistakable sound, and highly evocative of the wild moors, marshes and bogs in northern and western parts of Britain, Ireland and mainland Europe which hold good populations of breeding snipe.

The weather seems to influence the occurrence and intensity of bleating, just as it also appears to affect the woodcock's roding behaviour. On very mild days in February I have occasionally heard a snipe bleat, only to hear nothing further during weeks of ensuing cold and rain until the milder weather of late March and the start of the breeding season proper. Snipe are also said to bleat occasionally when on migration, but the most remarkable instances I know are of *dead* snipe bleating.

I first heard of this phenomenon from the late Sir Norman Stronge of Tynan Abbey in Northern Ireland, a passionately keen sportsman and an acutely observant naturalist. He told of how he had been shooting many years ago in the west of Ulster and of a driven snipe which he shot and which drummed as it fell. Recently I too had personal experience of this 'swansong' by a shot snipe. I shot a high-flying snipe which did not fall vertically but which came down very hard hit, at a steep angle. It drummed momentarily as it fell, to be picked up by my retriever only a few seconds later. It was quite dead, and I can only assume that the fatal shot induced some sort of involuntary spasm which caused the tail feathers to flare outwards to the critical angle, resulting in a fleeting burst of drumming as the dead bird fell.

The snipe is a ground-nesting bird and its choice of nest site is usually nothing more than a small depression in the ground, which is almost always lined with grass. It is not surprising that snipe nest on or close to bogs, marshes and other wetlands but the nest itself will be on a dry, well drained spot. Nests can be difficult to find, not because they are concealed under cover, although this may occasionally happen, but owing to the coloration of the eggs or of the motionless snipe as it incubates them. A full clutch will

25 *A well camouflaged snipe incubates her clutch of four eggs among bracken and dead grasses on a hill in Inverness-shire. Incubation takes around 20 days, and the female will usually be rejoined by the male as the first eggs hatch.*

normally consist of four eggs, well camouflaged by a rich blotching and speckling of browns on a greenish-grey background.

As is the case with woodcock, the incubation of the eggs is carried out by the female alone and will normally last for about 20 days. Unlike the woodcock, however, when the male bird only stays with the female until the clutch of eggs is complete before he resumes his roding displays in the hope of mating with another female, the male snipe is present at the hatching of the eggs. He may well show increasing interest in the nest as the time of hatching approaches. For a day or so before breaking out of its egg the well developed chick calls with a high piping note and this sound may be an influence in drawing the male back close to the nest. He is there when the chicks hatch and, despite his apparent unconcern during the incubation period, he has never been far away and will readily help brood some of the newly hatched chicks. He is likely to show particular interest in those which hatch first and may assume responsibility for one or two of the older chicks. Post-war studies of various world-wide snipe subspecies have shown that the parents share the responsibility for brooding, feeding and rearing the young, and that males tend to assume the care of the first one or two chicks to hatch. However, on average, females will probably look after the majority of the chicks.

Newly hatched snipe chicks have disproportionately large bills and feet, and because the eggs do not hatch simultaneously – 'asynchronous hatching', to be technical – the older chicks dry out earlier, recover their strength after the exhausting exertions of breaking out of the egg, and become active well before their later-hatching siblings. The early chicks will be vigorous and active within an hour or so of hatching and often several hours before the later eggs have hatched. The adult will normally lead the young chicks away from the nest but there are a handful of intriguing reports of snipe being seen actually *carrying* their young. For woodcock this is now a well established and frequently observed phenomenon but it is probably an untypical form of behaviour, and appears to be exceptionally rare among snipe. In fact, the phenomenon has still to be confirmed.

A young snipe is on the move within hours of hatching and it may be difficult for the female to take care of it and brood it if she is still incubating one or more unhatched eggs. The readiness of the male to assume the care of such early-hatched wanderers undoubtedly helps their survival. The young chicks appear also to have an innate instinct for self-preservation which protects them. They will hide in any long vegetation which affords cover from the eyes of predators and this, combined with the natural camouflage of their plumage, can make them very difficult to locate. It is believed by some observers that the female has a special 'hide yourselves!' call by which she tells her chicks to scurry into cover when danger threatens. Another survival aid may be the fact that, at this time in their lives, both adults and chicks appear to give off little or no scent. At most times of the year snipe have, from a dog's point of view, a very strong scent. Many pointers and setters begin their working careers on snipe, which have a scent out of all proportion to their small size. Even breeds like retrievers and spaniels, which are much less aware of the air-scent given off by distant birds, will often learn to pick up the scent of a snipe at some range. But experienced 'bird dogs' with proven noses for snipe will often miss an incubating or brooding snipe totally, and this must be an important survival advantage for small ground-nesters which might otherwise fall victim to predators like foxes.

On one occasion in early May my labrador bitch, an experienced snipe finder, almost tripped over a snipe and chicks on heather moorland in Ireland. The bird scaaped and zigzagged off upwind, circling round and calling as the dog quested in the short heather, apparently rather nonplussed by a very weak and uncertain scent. Suddenly her head went down twice and she galloped back to me with an 'I've got something for you' look on her face. On the command 'Give' she gently opened her mouth and out popped two tiny snipe chicks, barely larger than the top joint of my thumb, slightly damp but otherwise unharmed. I was able quickly to locate the spot from which my bitch had brought the chicks and to return them to it. Dog and master retreated behind a peat hag some way off and had the satisfaction of seeing the adult bird circle down and silently rejoin the chicks. There had been no sign of egg fragments or other indications of a nest, although the chicks were clearly not more than a day old, so this may have been a male which had taken responsibility for two older chicks. The scent must have been virtually non-existent, for an upwind approach in good scenting conditions with a proven snipe-finding dog had given no advance warning of the birds' presence.

The snipe chick grows quite rapidly, and will normally be capable of short, weak flights 17 or 18 days after hatching, and by this time it will weigh almost as much as its parent. At two months old the length of the wings and the bill will be the same as the adult bird, and by this time the young snipe should have its full first-year plumage. By then the post-breeding adults should be into their summer moulting phase.

Snipe chicks will peck and pick at potential food within hours of hatching but they are heavily dependent upon their parents for food, especially during the first few days of life. The adults feed their chicks on a wide range of worms, larvae and invertebrate items, many of which will have been broken up and softened by the adult to make feeding easier for its young. But snipe chicks will chase and peck at beetles and insects from an early age and their diet will gradually include an increasing proportion of these items. Until it is larger and stronger and has achieved full development of the bill, which is a highly specialised feeding tool, the young snipe cannot cope satisfactorily with the business of probing for food items in the soil.

Wintering snipe are birds of the wetlands, probing for worms and other invertebrates in mud and ooze, under shallow surface water. In late spring and summer, however, their diet contains a much higher proportion of the insect and invertebrate life to be found above the surface of the ground.

There are several reasons for this. Fly and insect life is more abundant in spring and summer on the areas where snipe breed and moult than on the flooded wetlands of winter, and so there is a seasonal abundance of insects like beetles and caterpillars. Often in summer the ground may be too hard for easy probing, even by adult snipe. In the exceptionally dry summers of 1976 and 1984 snipe were breeding and feeding on moor and heathland areas where the ground was so dry after months of drought that probing was impossible. All the damp patches and even the perennially wet sphagnum moss were quite dried out, yet numbers of snipe were present and subsisting largely on the available above-ground food. In the early days of the grouse shooting season we shot a number of snipe and their stomach contents were found to include large quantities of craneflies or daddy-long-legs. Myriads of these insects had been swarming on the grassy parts of our moor, which was aridly dry and offered no scope for feeding by probing.

A summer snipe is often regarded as a poor sporting target and an almost worthless table bird. This is largely owing to the adult bird's loss of weight and condition following the twin stresses of breeding and moulting. A snipe shot on a grouse moor in mid-August will be either a recently fledged juvenile which has not yet reached fully adult physical condition or a post-breeding adult which has not fully completed its moult. In either case the bird will probably be weaker in flight and thinner than an autumn or winter snipe. By the time of the full moon in September both adults and juveniles will be in good fettle to face the oncoming winter, and British and Irish residents will have been joined by a proportion of the winter immigrant population. By the October full moon the British Isles wintering population will be near its peak and it is then that the snipe is at its most sporting as a quarry species and its most delicious as a plump morsel for any gourmet. To most sportsmen and naturalists the wintering habits of the snipe are rather more familiar than its summer behaviour. Anyone lucky enough to live in a snipe-favoured area will be able to see a good deal of their comings and goings and will know where and when they are most likely to be encountered. Wet ground is an absolute prerequisite for wintering snipe, which feed by probing in soft, worm-rich earth, but they will generally avoid areas which have been flooded to a depth of more than an inch or so.

The edges of river banks and lake shores may provide linear feeding areas, but the classic snipe bog comprises an extensive marshy area, permanently wet but with only the shallowest of flood water. Open areas will ideally be interspersed with clumps of longer grasses, rushes and other vegetation where snipe can find cover and lie up in drier conditions to rest between feeding sessions. Habitat management to encourage numbers of snipe should take account of this and aim to create a patchwork of short vegetation for feeding and a number of areas of longer, uncut or unburnt growth for shelter, cover and as resting places. The old practice in many western areas of Britain and Ireland was to put cattle and other stock out to graze in summer on the bogs and marshes, areas which were probably too wet to be grazed in winter. Beasts which were tethered on the bogs naturally grazed out circular patches and as they were moved they created a pattern of well grazed areas interspersed with longer, ungrazed vegetation. The beasts' manure also helped to enrich the soil and enhanced its invertebrate life, and everything combined to create a very favourable habitat for wintering snipe a few months later.

Artificial snipe bogs can be created by the deliberate flooding of an area, especially water meadows which have been retained as permanent pasture and which are therefore likely to have a high invertebrate soil fauna. In parts of southern England some excellent snipe marshes have been temporarily created by regulating the sluices and hatches on chalkland streams to create shallow flooding. If the ground is rich in worms and disturbed as rarely as possible, large numbers of snipe may be drawn to such areas. Experiments to improve habitat for snipe have included the spreading or spraying of liquid or dried animal blood over the bogs, but the effectiveness of this rather gruesome technique has not

26 *Snipe feed by probing in soft mud which is rich in earthworms and insect larvae. Wet pastures, grazed and manured by cattle in summer, can be ideal winter feeding grounds for snipe. Frozen ground prevents them from feeding, and the drainage of wetlands is destroying much of their essential wintering habitat in Britain and Ireland.*

been fully proven. But decaying organic matter such as livestock manure will definitely enrich the soil and help to promote a rich and abundant source of worms and other food species attractive to snipe.

The feeding actions of snipe involve two basic types of probing, one much faster and less deliberate than the other. At certain times snipe can be seen to feed by probing deeply and thoroughly, feeling carefully for underground food items with that sensitive prehensile bill which enables it to identify, grasp and eat all but the biggest food items without withdrawing its bill fully from the ground. This kind of feeding may involve six or eight probes per minute and snipe will feed in an arc or sometimes almost a full circle when conditions are calm and there is no strong tail wind to get up under their feathers. Normally, like most birds, snipe will tend to feed and stand with their heads into the wind.

The other feeding style of snipe is much busier and more restless, with a probing rate of perhaps thirty or forty probes per minute. The quest for food appears to be much more random and less ponderous as the birds run about, often in small groups. As other snipe flight in to join a feeding group, or if a bird of another species appears, there may be a brief 'warning off' display of tail-fanning and wing-fluttering.

Snipe are voracious feeders and maintain a high rate of food intake. Rich and abundant worm and invertebrate food results in the strong, fast-flying, agile and plump-fleshed bird which is so prized by the gun and the gastronome. But snipe cannot cope with freezing conditions and will lose weight and physical condition very rapidly indeed if their wet feeding areas are permanently frozen. They will show a marked deterioration in condition after two or three days of continuous frost and very cold conditions will bring about wholesale movements of snipe populations in search of unfrozen grounds. At such times they will be forced to feed by the side of any remaining unfrozen watercourses, in muddy patches where cattle have broken up the ground and indeed almost anywhere which offers the opportunity of food. Prolonged cold spells such as occurred in the winters of 1947 and 1963 can result in massive mortality of snipe. Careful records kept by a number of the more important Irish snipe shoots showed that the repercussions of the 1963 freeze-up were evident in the greatly reduced numbers of snipe seen and shot during the ensuing few seasons, and it was seven or eight years before the wintering populations on those areas came back to pre-1963 levels.

In Britain and Ireland prolonged freezing conditions are still the exception, and their effects are comparatively short-lived, but the impact of a freeze-up on snipe habitat shows how vital it is that these birds should have suitable wet, frost-free feeding grounds if they are to overwinter successfully. Britain and Ireland have always been important wintering areas for a high percentage of Europe's snipe, and that proportion seems to be increasing. Noticeably fewer migrants now stop to moult and winter in the Netherlands and Denmark, chiefly owing to drainage and habitat loss, but instead migrate straight to the British Isles, thereby increasing our wintering populations and making Britain and Ireland of even greater international importance than hitherto as a winter haven for snipe.

This gives us in these islands a heavy responsibility for ensuring that sufficient suitable habitat is retained for wintering snipe. Yet anyone who is familiar with the rural scene in the western areas of Britain and Ireland must be aware of how much traditional snipe ground has been lost in recent years, chiefly as a result of drainage. Throughout western Scotland, many parts of Wales, the West Country and Ireland there has been a widespread and growing tendency to drain areas which have formerly always been wet and therefore attractive to snipe. Generous subsidies and the development of easily installed perforated drainage pipes have brought about the loss of large areas of former snipe bog. Often the drainage had been agriculturally and economically justified, turning wet ground into profitable pasture or even arable land. But this is not always the case. There have been many instances where drainage has failed to bring the Midas touch to land which has still remained basically unprofitable to the landowner. Once the drainage is complete it is too late to go back. Habitat has been lost, the snipe, duck and other water birds have gone, and the whole wetland ecosystem has been destroyed. The vegetation and insect life will have been changed fundamentally and permanently, and the farmer may be no better off after all. This sort of ill advised drainage results in losses all round, and highlights the importance of draining only those areas where a clear agricultural advantage will result. However handsome the grants and subsidy incentives may be, a drainage operation should not be carried out lightly, and the environmental consequences should be carefully assessed.

Although bog drainage is not a new phenomenon, it has recently been joined by another potential threat to snipe and their traditional wetland habitat. The old, labour-intensive and often back-breaking business of cutting peat or turf from blanket bogs by hand is being replaced by the use of a mechanical 'mole' turf-cutter, which removes the peat by extruding it in long tubular cores. These machines are increasingly being used in parts of Scotland and Ireland, and to the casual onlooker they seem to remove the peat while leaving the bog looking virtually untouched. In fact, while the surface is not actually cut away, the extrusion of the underlying peat results in major waterlogging of the bog, making it much wetter than before. It is probably still too early to say what the long-term consequences of this type of peat extraction will be, but a greater amount of virtually stagnant water will presumably result in changes in the insect and invertebrate fauna and the natural flora of the bogs, thereby bringing about a significant alteration in their general ecology. What have been attractive wintering areas for snipe and other species, and places of great botanical and entomological interest, may become progressively less attractive after the peat extraction machine has done its work. Another consideration is the fact that extraction with this machinery invariably takes place in spring and summer, when the vehicle with its large, low-ground-pressure tyres drives to and fro across the surface of the bogs. This not only represents a major disturbance of the area but could be quite fatal to ground-nesting birds, which risk having their nests and eggs crushed by the machinery. Technological progress which now enables the landowner to extract and sell valuable peat from an area which may hitherto have been unworked or unworkable seems once again to have militated against wildlife and the natural environment.

A great many important wetlands have been designated Sites of Special Scientific Interest, usually for their flora or their value to wetland birds, especially wintering migrants. This is only one aspect of the much larger issue of how we reconcile environmental conservation with viable agriculture and other economically productive forms of land use. It would be quite unreasonable to prevent a landowner from draining unprofitable land without compensating him adequately. But we also have a national and international responsibility to ensure a future for snipe and other wintering migrants and the wetland habitats upon which they depend.

10. *The Woodcock*

The woodcock is, quite simply, an oddity. Its silent and mysterious life, its twisting flight, its delicious flesh, the excitement which it causes when it appears on a shooting day are only some of the curious aspects of a very remarkable game bird.

In simple numerical terms, woodcock are on the fringes of the game-shooting world, a tiny drop in an ocean dominated by the pheasant. Pheasants actually represent over 85 per cent of all game birds shot in Britain each year, which puts partridge, grouse, blackgame and all the other game birds in very subordinate positions. But, happily, numbers are not everything, and if pheasants constitute the staple diet of the game shooter woodcock can certainly be regarded as a very special and much-coveted sporting treat.

Get together any group of sporting shooters and set them talking about their sport and the birds they love, and it will not be long before the discussion turns to woodcock. The excitement and enthusiasm which the woodcock stirs up in the sportsman's mind is a real indication of what a very special bird it is. But the extent to which it will figure in the gamebook is largely a matter of geography, for reasons which are explained by the bird's way of life, by its feeding methods and by its habitat preferences.

By setting aside some land and signing a sufficiently large cheque the sportsman can create a good pheasant shoot almost anywhere. The pheasant lends itself to the intensive rearing and specialised releasing methods which make possible these 'made to measure' shoots, and this largely explains why pheasants dominate the game-shooting scene so overwhelmingly.

Woodcock are a very different proposition. More than almost any other game bird they depend upon the right sort of habitat and are subject to the uncontrollable vagaries of the weather, the phases of the moon, and other factors over which man has little or no control. He who goes out with dog and gun specifically in pursuit of woodcock is taking part in a true 'field sport', a world away from the carefully organised, accurately calculated hundred-bird pheasant day.

We can learn a great deal about the woodcock and its ways simply by studying the physical make-up of the bird itself. The long bill clearly indicates a bird which feeds by probing in soft mud and ooze, and naturally we classify woodcock among the waders. They have almost certainly evolved over the ages from a true wading ancestor, but their legs are proportionately shorter than those of snipe or other long-legged shore birds like the redshank or godwit. That long and sensitive bill has a flexible, prehensile tip, with the upper mandible a few millimetres longer than the lower. Recent research by the Game Conservancy reveals that woodcock feed principally on earthworms, but insect larvae and other invertebrates also figure in their diet.

The large, dark and lustrous eyes of the woodcock are another very prominent feature and the positioning of these eyes gives the bird almost 360° vision. These qualities combine to make the woodcock well equipped to deal with poor light and to take effective evasive action against predators.

The woodcock's body is stout and sturdy, with the rounded wings of a bird which can accelerate rapidly away from danger. Its plump thighs also assist this, by providing the powerful upward thrust necessary for a 'vertical take-off' spring into flight.

The plumage is a marvel of natural camouflage, a superb visually disruptive pattern of buff, browns and black, which merges perfectly with the litter of dead leaves and bracken in winter woodlands.

In the late 1970s Dr Graham Hirons of the Game Conservancy began a detailed five-year research project to investigate the wintering habits and breeding biology of woodcock in Britain. This was the first serious attempt to look scientifically at woodcock biology in the British Isles, with a view to dispelling and clarifying some of the many fables and enigmas associated with woodcock and providing sportsmen with proven facts drawn from meticulous scientific study. Woodcock shooters, like all field sportsmen, have always taken a close interest in the natural history of their quarry species, but factual discoveries have often been obscured by inaccurate observation, fables and folklore. In the 1980s only sound scientific understanding is good enough to enable sportsmen and environmentalists to work effectively to ensure the future well-being of species like the woodcock.

Graham Hirons's woodcock study, which employed the latest radio-telemetry technology, showed that wintering woodcock spend the daylight hours roosting in cover. Low bracken and brambles, gorse, laurel and rhododendron shrubs and other evergreens, and even long heather on the open hill are favoured as daytime roosting cover, with a

27 *The large, lustrous eyes and long bill are distinctive features of the woodcock. This female is well camouflaged as she sits on her clutch of four eggs. Breeding woodcock prefer broad-leaved woodland, especially ash and sycamore, where the soil holds abundant earthworms and other invertebrate food items. The female and her chicks will feed by day on the floor of the woodland around the nest site.*

decided preference shown for dark, moist, frost-free places. These are the spots from which the beaters' disturbance or the spaniels' questing noses will flush roosting woodcock on a shooting day. When undisturbed, woodcock will roost until dusk. As the light fails they will fly out, often along well established flight lines, to feed during the hours of darkness. Damp pastures and meadows are typical feeding grounds, and the manure of grazing cattle and sheep helps to promote the rich earthworm and invertebrate fauna which woodcock love. Radio-tagged birds on a study area in Cornwall flew an average distance of half a mile from their daytime roosts to their nocturnal feeding grounds.

Woodcock enthusiasts have always puzzled over the fact that birds shot in daylight hours have little or no stomach and gut contents – hence the curious tradition of cooking and serving woodcock without drawing them. Graham Hirons's research confirmed that wintering birds do not feed by daylight but gorge themselves at night on large quantities of earthworms, insect larvae, and similar invertebrates. Birds trapped or shot under licence at night were found to be crammed with earthworms, while those shot by day had digested and excreted almost all their previous night's food, leaving stomach and gut almost empty.

Feeding was found to be especially voracious during the first hour after dark, with periods of resting and feeding alternating through the night until the birds flighted back to their daytime roosts at the first hint of daybreak. This pattern is typical of the sedentary wintering population so long as the weather remains mild. Hard frost is the enemy of birds which must probe into soft earth and mud for their food, and severe winter weather forces woodcock to move on in search of milder, frost-free feeding grounds. This accounts for the general migration pattern of European woodcock, which breed prolifically in Scandinavia and northern Europe in spring, later to move away as frost and snow drive the birds south and west in search of milder wintering areas. In normal winters the major south-westerly migrations take place on the full moon in October and November, as the birds take advantage of the moonlight to assist their long-distance journeys. Tired and ill-conditioned birds can be seen when a 'fall' of migrant woodcock lands on the east coast of England or Scotland, but rest and rich feeding will restore their vigour and plump condition within a day or two.

Bouts of very severe cold and winter storms will force settled and sedentary wintering woodcock to move away, and the exceptionally severe winters of 1947, 1963 and 1981 provided instances of this. With most of western Europe and Great Britain in the grip of severe frost, huge concentrations of woodcock were to be found in Cornwall, the Hebrides and in Ireland – all enjoying milder conditions owing to the benign influences of the warmer waters of the North Atlantic Drift.

These mild 'Celtic fringes' of western Scotland, west Wales, Ireland and Brittany are the traditional haunts of the biggest wintering populations of Europe's woodcock, and it is in localised areas such as Islay in the Hebrides, and the coverts of Galway and Mayo in Ireland that the biggest historical bags of woodcock have been made. In late Victorian times conditions were especially favourable for record-breaking bags of 'cock, when the generally treeless landscapes of western Scotland and Ireland contained just a few coverts which attracted unnaturally high densities of hard-pressed woodcock. Today's extensive plantations of commercial softwoods now harbour large but thinly distributed populations of wintering woodcock. The prodigious bags of 'cock shot a century ago would simply not be attainable today, with birds less densely concentrated but probably more numerous than ever before. It is a very desirable development to see these vast and all-too-lifeless monocultures of conifers providing suitable wintering habitat for today's visiting populations of woodcock.

With the coming of longer days in spring the bulk of Britain's and Ireland's wintering 'cock migrate back to their breeding grounds around the Baltic. But a proportion of woodcock remain with us to breed – perhaps 10 per cent, and with indications that the proportion is gradually increasing. The spring and summer breeding behaviour of woodcock differs in some important respects from their winter routine.

Graham Hirons's detailed study of nesting woodcock in a woodland study area in Derbyshire uncovered many important facts about the breeding biology of this species. Most important, it showed that woodcock do not pair off and that the males, although polygamous, do not hold and defend territories in the conventional sense of the word. The male woodcock's characteristic display takes the form of a dawn and dusk 'roding flight', with most activity at dusk and of increasing duration as the hours of daylight lengthen. While wintering woodcock are silent except for a click of wings on

28   *Male woodcock undertake dawn and dusk roding displays, flying around over suitable nesting habitat with a distinctive 'croak and* twisk' *calls. A dominant male will display persistently and may drop down to mate with a succession of females, each of which will have taken up its own nesting site.*

rising, displaying males in spring are highly vocal. Their roding flights are accompanied by two unmistakable calls – a deep, almost frog-like croak, and a high-pitched, squeaking 'twisk'.

The most dominant males display for long periods over prime nesting cover, where females have already taken nesting sites. The roding male will drop down to join a receptive female, will mate with her, and may remain for several days until a clutch of eggs – usually four in number – is complete. He will then probably resume his roding flights and may mate with another two or more females in due course.

Less dominant males either remain as a non-breeding reservoir of birds or will carry out roding flights over less favourable habitat and for shorter periods. When a dominant male is removed from circulation, either by having temporarily joined a female or as a result of death or injury, it will quickly be replaced by another male who will display over the same area, perhaps to be displaced later if the dominant male returns. Observations of roding behaviour have included many instances of apparent skirmishing between two and sometimes three roding males competing for 'air space' over the best breeding habitat.

The female bird incubates her eggs throughout the night and does not venture far from them by day. Graham Hirons observed that females rarely went further than 80 yards away from the nest and always by walking rather than flying.

The eggs are incubated and the young chicks cared for solely by the hen bird and the young are dependent upon their mother for several days after hatching. After that time mother and young will scratch around in search of worms on the forest floor. Optimum nesting habitat is therefore in woodlands with a high density of earthworms. Sycamore and ash woods with brambles and other light ground cover are particularly suitable, while mature pine woods are unsuitable owing to the low density of worms and other invertebrates on the forest floor.

Research has therefore shown that the winter feeding pattern of daytime roosting and active nocturnal feeding is replaced in late spring and summer by nocturnal roosting and daytime feeding, both within the nesting woodland. This, together with an understanding of other aspects of woodcock biology, provides sportsmen and environmentalists with some of the background knowledge necessary to ensure that suitable breeding and wintering habitat is available for woodcock in the future.

For sportsmen there are important lessons to be learned, especially in the provision of attractive wintering areas to draw in suitable numbers of woodcock. In late Victorian and Edwardian times certain estates, principally in the milder western areas, maintained shoots specifically for woodcock. Gorse, laurel and rhododendron plantations close to moist, worm-rich pastures were carefully broken up with rides and tunnels to enable woodcock to flight in and out with ease.

29 *Britain and Ireland are hosts to large numbers of immigrant woodcock which come south to winter here in our mild climate. Woodcock will roost singly by day in woodland, scrub and other low cover, flighting out at dusk to feed on worm-rich pasture land and returning at first light to their daytime roost sites.*

Recent research has shown that the traditional and almost forgotten techniques of woodcock keepering are very effective in attracting and holding numbers of wintering woodcock. Coverts must also be kept quiet, for woodcock will not tolerate disturbance.

A great deal of important research has been done on woodcock in Britain and Europe in recent years, and it all helps to dispel some of the mystery and misunderstandings which in the past have surrounded this remarkable game bird. But more remains to be done if we are to acquire a really comprehensive understanding of woodcock biology. What is the breeding pattern of woodcock which breed in coniferous woods with low earthworm levels? Why do the males continue and increase the duration of their displaying flights even after peak nesting times? What has caused the post-war proliferation of short-billed individuals? What is the impact of hard winters and varying levels of shooting pressure on the woodcock population? These and many other questions remain to be answered.

As a species the woodcock has run against the general trend of our game birds in that it appears to be expanding its breeding range and increasing its wintering population in Britain and Ireland. Woodcock are now regularly seen roding and nesting, often in or around recently planted conifer forests, in areas where their nesting has not previously been recorded. The availability of large areas of quiet, undisturbed roosting habitat bordered by invertebrate-rich feeding grounds is encouraging more woodcock to winter with us, even though they still occur at comparatively low densities and it can be difficult to get to grips with them on a shooting day.

The recent developments in our understanding of the breeding strategy of the species – once thought to be monogamous but now known, in technical terms, to be 'successively polygynous' – are a major step forward in unravelling some of the mystery which still obscures many aspects of the bird's ways. The implications of our new-found understanding for the practical management of wood-cock are very limited. Frost-free winter weather is not something we can influence, and the availability of adequate earthworm and other invertebrate food in the soil is largely a matter of agricultural land use, soil types and tree species in woodland. The effort necessary to manipulate and promote these to encourage an unpredictable and largely migratory wintering population would be uneconomic and out of all proportion to any sporting return which might be obtained.

Certain favoured areas like the Hebrides, west Wales and parts of Cornwall will always benefit and produce larger annual harvests of woodcock if the daytime roosting habitat is managed by tunnelling and the creation of rides and 'skylights' to let woodcock flight in and out easily and to enable the beating party on a shooting day to put a high proportion of the woodcock over the guns. In most other areas woodcock will continue to make an appearance in greater or lesser numbers according to the vagaries of their migratory movements, which we do not wholly understand, and the influences of the winds, the full moon and the weather.

Severe winter weather in late December and January has led to shooting bans in Britain and the Irish Republic in 1981–2 and again in 1985. These have been implemented in accordance with criteria agreed between government departments and interested conservation, field sports and bird protection organisations, and the only part of the British Isles which has not been affected by statutory bans at these times has been Northern Ireland, owing to constitutional and legislative difficulties following the implementation of direct rule from Westminster. With the arrival of the Northern Ireland Wildlife Order 1985 provision now exists for the introduction of shooting bans based on agreed criteria.

But what are the effects of really hard winters on woodcock? Do shooting bans make a worthwhile contribution to the survival of the species when weather conditions are known to be very unfavourable to other birds like snipe, duck and geese?

There is considerable evidence to indicate that the onset of really cold weather triggers off a positive response in woodcock, which increase their food intake and build up their physical condition in preparation for the leaner times ahead. They also undertake mass migrations away from frozen areas in search of milder wintering grounds, and this was vividly demonstrated by the huge influx of woodcock from continental Europe to the milder parts of Britain and Ireland in the severe winter of 1981–2 and again in January 1985, when sudden and extreme frosts swept across the continent just at the time of the full moon. East Anglia and the north-east coasts of England and Scotland reported large falls of immigrant 'cock on these occasions. These hard-weather immigrants were inevitably debilitated and low in weight immediately after their flight but generally recovered condition within forty-eight hours and then dispersed widely across the country.

Winter residents and new immigrants may still find it difficult to adopt a regular regime of daytime roosting and night-time feeding in the sort of conditions experienced in December 1981, January 1982 and January 1985. However, they will readily adapt to more irregular and opportunistic feeding, flying about in search of unfrozen ground and often feeding in broad daylight, as they do in spring and summer in their breeding woods.

A slight daytime thaw will open up springs, drains and other wet ground which refreezes solid at night, and woodcock make good use of these spots and unfrozen stream banks, muddy fields broken up by cattle and lightly frozen ground beneath evergreens such as rhododendrons, laurel and holly. As a species they display a remarkable capacity for finding adequate food and maintaining good bodily condition at times when duck are very hard pressed and when snipe may already be dying of starvation in large numbers.

From an examination of several thousands of woodcock shot in frosty conditions just before and after ban periods I personally have found only a tiny percentage of birds to be noticeably thin, and less than one in a hundred to show signs of significant emaciation.

Hard weather inevitably results in bird mortality, and woodcock are not an exception to this rule. Woodcock shooting in freezing conditions will increase the local proportions of 'cock shot, but is unlikely to change the total bag size across the range of the species. When a high proportion of Continental woodcock are driven temporarily to Britain by bad weather, mortality on migration will be considerable and those shot here will probably not be as numerous as those which would have been shot in countries like France, Belgium and Germany had they remained there. Current levels of shooting throughout Europe are regarded by biologists as having no effect on total populations. Weather and the stresses of migration will cause much more significant levels of mortality and a great many birds which are not shot during periods of statutory bans will die anyway. I received reports of numbers of woodcock found dead from starvation on the coasts of Normandy and Brittany in January 1985. Others migrated en masse to Britain and there were only a handful of reports of thin or starved birds anywhere in the British Isles in the winter of 1984-5.

The scientists' message seems to be that when woodcock occur at high densities in frost-free areas, shooting is unlikely to make any significant difference to their general rate of survival or to the following spring's breeding population. Mortality is compensatory and a shot woodcock cannot die later from any other 'natural' cause.

It has been argued that the shooting of woodcock at a time when some other species are hard pressed by severe weather may cause undue disturbance to other birds. It is difficult to see how this can be the case, since the winter habitat of woodcock is areas of woodland and scrub which are primarily pheasant coverts. The majority of woodcock shot in Britain are bagged on pheasant covert shoots and they tend not to share habitat with species like duck and geese which should not therefore suffer disturbance. Woodcock do not flock, except on migration, and disturbance on shooting days is therefore to individual birds. Since pheasant shoots continue in shooting-ban periods individual woodcock will therefore be disturbed in any event. Only when woodcock are driven to the foreshore would woodcock shooting disturb other species which might suffer in consequence, and the occurrence of woodcock on the sea-shore has only been observed in exceptionally prolonged and severe winters, such as that of 1881 described by Sir Ralph Payne-Gallway in *The Fowler in Ireland*.

Based on its detailed study of the biology of wintering woodcock, the Game Conservancy submitted its view to the Advisory Committee on Birds in 1982 that the shooting of woodcock in woodland and on farmland should be exempted from future cold-weather bans. That opinion still stands, based as it is on the best available scientific information.

The response of woodcock to hard weather and their future in general in the changed and changing environment of the 1980s must continue to receive close attention from game biologists and sportsmen, to ensure that we maintain a careful watching brief on this important species. Meanwhile, in the light of what we have learned from recent studies, one can take heart from the fact that the woodcock shows all the signs of maintaining and expanding its British and European populations at a time when so many other species are in serious decline.

11. *The Brown Hare*

The hare is the only mammal which is regarded as game by the British sportsman who pursues his quarry with a shotgun. Although a game licence is necessary to take or kill deer, deer are not game in the strict legal sense of the word and are in any case in a rather different sporting category. Their effective management and control involves the specialist skills of the stalker with his rifle or, in certain areas like Exmoor, hunting with hounds.

The brown hare (*Lepus capensis*) has a very ancient and worthy tradition as a sporting quarry. Its pursuit with greyhounds and other similar breeds of 'gazehounds' or 'longdogs' which hunt by sight is an age-old sport, and the keeping of gazehounds like the greyhound and the saluki can be traced back for thousands of years, especially in the

detailed records of the Egyptian and other ancient Mediterranean civilisations. In Britain hare hunting with beagles,
harriers and other breeds of hound which hunt by scent and
rely upon their noses rather than upon direct pursuit of a
visible quarry has been well established since Norman times
and, like deer hunting, has a much longer history than fox
hunting. The familiar style of modern fox hunting is a
comparatively recent development within the last 250 years,
although it now dominates the hound sports scene in Britain.
That was not always the case. Many medieval and early
modern writers gave pride of place to the hare. Edward, Duke
of York, wrote a celebrated treatise on hunting about the year
1406 entitled *The Master of Game* and in it he gives the hare
precedence over all other game: '. . . the hare is the king of all
venery. For certain it is the most marvellous beast that is.'
That shadowy figure Dame Juliana Berners, mysterious
authoress of *The Book of St Albans* (1486), the first printed
book on field sports in the English language, also hails the
hare as 'Kyng of venery . . . the marvellest beast that is in any
londe'.

The literature on the hare in sport is extensive and can be
traced back into classical antiquity and beyond. Xenophon,
an Athenian of the fourth century BC and a pupil of Socrates,
wrote the *Cynegetica,* a treatise on hare hunting, in which he
extols the pleasures of the sport and dwells at length on the
Spartans' pursuit of the hare with scenting hounds. We know
that the Celts and Saxons kept large gazehounds, ancestors of
today's greyhounds and deerhounds, to hunt hares and in
the later Middle Ages Geoffrey Chaucer's worldly-wise monk
– perhaps the prototype of the sporting parson? – is portrayed
as a passionately keen hare hunter:

> Greyhoundes he hadde as swifte as fowle in flight;
> Of pryking and of huntyng for the hare
> Was all his lust; for no cost would he spare.

The hunting of hares with small private packs of beagles,
often owned by private individuals of relatively modest

means such as the minor gentry and the clergy, formed the
basis of all hunting with hounds during the seventeenth and
eighteenth centuries. The dominance of hare hunting and the
affection and enthusiasm which it inspired in many sporting
people is best summed up in Wilfrid Scawen Blunt's poem
'The Old Squire':

> I like the hunting of the hare
> Better than that of the fox;
> ... I like the hunting of the hare;
> It brings me day by day
> The memory of old days as fair;
> With dead men past away.
>
> I like the hunting of the hare;
> New sports I hold in scorn.
> *I like to be as my fathers were,*
> *In the days ere I was born.*

Fox hunting, by comparison, is almost a *parvenu* among
hound sports.

The brown hare has always been a common sight on
Britain's lowlands. Its obvious elegance and grace, its
timidity and speed, and its curious antics in spring have
attracted the affectionate interest of countrymen, and the
hare is one of our best loved mammals. But it has also been
the focus for a great deal of superstition and around it has
accumulated a great body of folklore and legend, much of it
sinister and vaguely menacing.

A full account of the hare's mythological significance
would fill a book in itself, but this creature became drawn
into a system of ancient beliefs about evil, witchcraft and the
occult largely because of many misunderstandings about its
basic biology and habits. Greek and Roman writers on
natural history, including Aristotle, Hippocrates, Pliny and
Aelian, claimed that hares could change their sex, becoming
male and female in alternate years, and that both sexes could
give birth. These beliefs persisted virtually unchanged and

unchallenged into the sixteenth and seventeenth centuries, when writers like Topsell, Rondelet and even our own learned Sir Thomas Browne of Norwich continued to promote the idea that hares were in some way androgynous.

The hare is intimately linked with tales and beliefs about witches, and this has resulted in a distinct wariness which still persists in many country communities today. Hares as witches' familiars and beliefs about witches taking the shape of hares in the daytime are just two of the commoner ways in which the occult link between hares and witches is made in many folk tales throughout the British Isles.

Modern British game shooting concentrates overwhelmingly upon birds, with pheasants, grouse and the partridge occupying pride of place. This contrasts with the attitude of most other European sportsmen, by whom the hare is much more prized as a quarry species. What is for the British gun usually an extra or 'various' to add variety to the bag is a prized trophy to many European sportsmen, and increasing numbers of visitors from the Continent now come to Britain specifically for hare shooting. In many areas the hare can be a serious agricultural pest when populations reach high densities, and the annual February hare shoot has long been an established event in many arable farming communities. Traditionally such shoots involve a mass turn-out of dozens of local people, often armed with a bizarre variety of guns, and such events have never been noted for the discipline and strict safety procedures which characterise other forms of driven game shooting in Britain. The large-scale hare shoots which took place as recently as the 1960s are now less common, largely because of changes in the pattern of farming and something of a general country-wide decline in hare numbers, but where hare shoots are still necessary to cull the population in the interest of agriculture the guns may well now be visiting European sportsmen who pay for their hare shooting, thereby providing welcome additional revenue for the landowner. The overseas sportsman, whatever his quarry, always represents a valuable economic asset, especially to remote rural communities, with hotels, guest-houses and other tourist-related activities benefiting from free-spending sportsmen who bring in valuable foreign currency. Sporting attitudes and traditions vary from country to country, but few British sportsmen derive any pleasure from a shooting day when hares are the sole quarry.

The hare is unlikely to be mistaken for any other animal, except perhaps the rabbit, but the hare has so many distinctive characteristics and behavioural traits that confusion ought not to arise. Most obvious of all is its much greater size; at more than 7 pounds in weight it is over twice as heavy as the biggest of adult rabbits. The long, black-tipped ears are also a sure identifying sign, and the hare's long-legged, bounding action as it moves is quite different from the hop-and-scamper movements of the rabbit. Specific distinguishing marks apart, there is something about the general make-up or 'jizz' of the two species which makes them quite unmistakable under most circumstances to anyone who is at all familiar with the British countryside. As its name suggests, the fur of the brown hare is predominantly brown in colour in contrast with the paler and rather greyish coat of the rabbit. The rich brown of the hare's winter coat is particularly striking.

Outside Britain the brown hare enjoys a very extensive international distribution throughout almost all of lowland Europe and eastwards as far as China. To this natural range we must add areas of Australia and New Zealand and parts of North and South America where the brown hare has been successfully introduced by man. Throughout its range the hare favours arable land, although the extent to which it also makes use of woodlands has only become clear in the light of some quite recent research. It is generally true to say that brown hare populations in Britain are much higher in the drier and predominantly arable lowlands of the south and east than in the wetter areas of permanent pasture in the west. This pattern of distribution is confirmed by the observations of countrymen and naturalists and is clearly reflected in the results of the annual national game census organised by the Game Conservancy. This measures the relative abundance or scarcity of game species by the numbers shot each year on a large sample of estates, farms and organised shoots. From this census we learn that the rich arable lands of East Anglia, the east Midlands and the arable areas of north-east Scotland sustain hares at three or more times the density of the pasture lands of the West Country, Wales and north-west England.

Light, well drained land which is favourable for intensive arable farming seems also to suit the hare. It is highly susceptible to the parasitic disease coccidiosis, which is commoner in a damp climate and on heavy soils. Hares are reluctant to share their home range with livestock, particularly cattle, and detailed observations have shown that they will go out of their way to avoid fields containing cattle and may not return to them until some days after the stock have been removed. Hares show a marked antipathy towards livestock, rather in the same way as roe deer, which will generally avoid areas where sheep have been put out to graze.

The former superabundance of brown hares, which necessitated some enormous culls by shooting earlier this century, began to take a downward turn in the 1960s. This was commented on by observant countrymen and their impressions were confirmed by the data analysed in the National Game Census. Clear signs of a country-wide decline caused general concern among sportsmen and the Game Conservancy's team of game biologists conceived and set up the major Hare Research Project which began in 1980. All the available data pointed to a steady reduction in the number of hares being shot in all parts of Britain since 1961 and this was correctly interpreted as evidence that hare populations were in general decline. In preparing to investigate the ecology of the brown hare and to identify the reasons for its decline scientists were particularly anxious to assess the impact of intensive modern farming regimes and also the effects of predation. This British project complemented a great deal of research into hare biology which has been carried out by other European biologists and sportsmen.

Two parallel studies were set up, in one of which a local population of hares was studied in detail while other work consisted of a comparative study of hare populations in several different lowland farming areas, each with its own pattern of farming and game management. While the latter study showed how hares fared under a variety of different circumstances, the detailed local study was to give biologists unprecedently intimate knowledge of the daily lives of a number of individual hares.

Detailed and reliable scientific research is costly, but funds for this three-year project came not only from the coffers of the Natural Environment Research Council but also as voluntary donations from the field sports community, including members of the Game Conservancy, the British Field Sports Society, the Coursing Supporters Club and the sporting press. This is only one example of how sportsmen are always eager and willing to support game research to help ensure a future for the game species which they love and on which our traditional field sports depend.

A study area in west Hampshire was chosen for the detailed investigation of hare behaviour, and it was first necessary to estimate the density of the hare population in that area and then to select a number of hares for close individual study. The accurate estimation of hare density is best achieved at night, when hares are most active in the open. While it is not uncommon to see hares in daylight, a high proportion of individuals will either be lying up in cover or so well concealed in grass or stubbles that they are not easy to detect. At night a very much higher proportion of hares are on the move, especially if the weather is not unduly cold, and so night is the best time to count them. The game biologists adopted a night-counting method originally developed in Sweden and involving the use of 100-watt spotlamps. The radius of the spotlight beam defined the limits of a circular sampling area and the presence of hares within the spotlight's arc was indicated by the tell-tale shine of their eyes – a good scientific application of a frequently used technique for taking hares and rabbits at night with

30 *Formerly a major agricultural pest which had to be culled annually by large-scale shooting, hares are now less abundant in many arable farming areas. Their breeding season antics and other mysterious ways, about which little was known until recently, made them the subject of more folklore and mythology than any other game species.*

lurchers. Hares were counted within the circular area of the lamp's field of illumination, and this method was used to build up a reliable indication of the density of the hare population on the farm in question. In the course of these night-time counts it was noticed that cold weather made hares much less active and consequently many fewer were to be seen on cool or frosty nights compared with milder, warmer weather.

Scientists are always anxious to know the reliability of their study methods, so a check was carried out on some areas where large-scale hare shoots took place. After hare shoots the precise bag totals were recorded and the disparity between the numbers seen on the 'before' and 'after' counts confirmed that night counting was indeed a reliable way of measuring variations in hare population density.

Modern technology has brought many benefits to game biologists working in the field, and in particular the development of miniature radio transmitters has been of incalculable value. The best way to keep tabs on an individual hare is to fit it with its own radio transmitter – but 'first catch your hare'! This had to be done in a way which would be both efficient and not unduly stressful for the hares involved. The timidity of hares is proverbial and they do not respond well to being caught and handled, which can be an enormously stressful procedure. The degree of stress they undergo is greatly minimised when the hare is caught and fitted with its radio transmitter at night, so a catching-up procedure was developed for use during the hours of darkness.

Long-nets, a very ancient and well tried method of catching hares, were set out singly and parallel to the fences or boundary hedges of fields and about ten yards out from the fence or hedge, with one end of the net drawn round to close it off. Hares were singled out with the spotlamp and a four-wheel drive vehicle was slowly manoeuvred so as to drive the hares towards the edge of the field and into the dead-end gap between the long-net and the fence. The vehicle was then moved into position to block off the remaining open end and hares then usually made an attempt to dash for freedom towards the middle of the field, thus becoming entangled in the meshes of the net. No one who has not tried to disentangle a large and active hare from a net in the dark can imagine what a tricky business it is! However, despite the struggles and entanglements, this method proved to be much less stressful and upsetting for the hares than when it was done in daylight, and the hares reacted much more favourably when they were released equipped with their new radio collars.

The radio-tagging involved the fitting of a lightweight

collar carrying a powerful miniature transmitter powered by a lithium cell battery and fitted with an aerial consisting of a thin loop of brass covered with PVC. This was the most effective of several designs which were tried and in certain cases it enabled scientists to track individual hares for periods of up to eight months, and at distances of a mile or slightly more.

Once 'bugged' in this way the radio-tagged hares could be followed day and night for periods of weeks and sometimes months on end. Fifteen hares were tagged and monitored over a seventeen-month period, which enabled the biologists to build up a unique picture of the hares' activities throughout the cycle of the farming year. A constant stream of radio signals from the hares, each of which could be identified from its personal radio frequency, made it possible to use a directional aerial to establish a fix on each animal. Two or more fixes enabled the hare's position to be plotted accurately and so a pattern of movement and behaviour began to emerge, which revealed the hares' preference for certain types of natural habitat and crops. Areas of short arable crops were especially favoured, while the hares showed a definite dislike for pastures with livestock and areas of long grass, except where the latter were used as cover during the daytime.

Woodland and hedges were found to be a favourite habitat, especially during the daytime, to an extent which had not previously been appreciated. Hares are most active at night and will lie up during the day in the cover of woodlands, low bushes and hedgerows and also some long crops. From here they will move at dusk to their night-time feeding areas. Some crops such as cereals were of changing significance to hares as they grew. Fields of short winter wheat, and especially of spring barley and stubble turnips, were used initially as feeding areas but as the crops grew and lengthened they were used less frequently, and then often as cover rather than for feeding. The hares' need for cover is well catered for by farmland which is broken up with a diversity of crop types and plenty of hedges, small woods and game copses, and odd corners with rough grasses, brambles and other cover.

Over much of lowland Britain the tendency in recent years has been for the removal of hedges on a large scale, to create very much bigger fields, and towards a general obsession with agricultural 'tidiness'. The country-wide trend towards hedge removal, field enlargement, extensive areas of mono-culture crops and the elimination of rough corners has militated against the habitat requirements of the hare. The Game Conservancy's study clearly showed that hares fare best where a wide range of crops and types of cover is available within a small area. Post-war agricultural trends have been in quite the opposite direction and today's farmland is a much less favourable habitat for hares than it was a generation ago.

Alongside the effect of changes in farmland habitat it was also necessary for scientists to study the impact of predation on hare numbers. The fox was the obvious predator to look at in this context, being our only wild mammal large enough to tackle a well grown leveret or an adult hare. The scientists' main study area was regularly searched for fox droppings, which were analysed in an effort to discover what the foxes had been eating. The results showed that foxes prey on hares to an extent which had never been realised before.

This study of the fox's diet compared its prey selection in winter – from October to March – with its summer fare during the period from April to September. A wide range of small mammals was regularly taken, including shrews, bank voles, field voles, house and field mice, harvest mice, rats and grey squirrels, and there was also an appreciable number of songbirds. But three categories of prey predominated – game birds, rabbits and hares. Game birds in the winter months made up a quarter of the foxes' food intake, and were the single most important food item, with rabbits representing about one-fifth of the total winter diet and hares rather less. During the summer, however, the prey pattern changed noticeably.

On the Hampshire study area hares were by far the most

important single prey species in summer, making up almost a third of the foxes' food. Rabbits came a close second, while game birds accounted for less than a tenth of the total, rather less than songbirds at that time of year. These food studies took place on one area with very few rabbits and it was estimated that one typical fox family – non-breeders, breeders and their cubs – would eat some 69 hares in the course of a full year. That is quite a dramatic figure, but the true impact of foxes on hare numbers may be even greater. Foxes need much more food in the spring, particularly in April and May when they have hungry families and growing cubs to feed. The foxes' peak food requirements therefore come before most hares have given birth to their leverets. Consequently a high proportion of hares killed by foxes in spring will be pregnant females, and so the loss is not merely that of a single female but of a mother and her young. An adult female hare can usually be expected to produce six or seven leverets in the late spring and summer months. We still do not know the precise extent to which fox predation affects the abundance of hares but all the evidence so far shows that hares have a poorer survival rate in areas where foxes are common.

Three years of detailed study went a long way towards explaining the hare's decline and taught us a lot about hare biology. No single cause was to blame but a number of circumstances had combined to bring about lower hare populations. The situation had been confused to some extent by exceptionally high hare numbers in the early 1960s following some excellent breeding seasons, and with the rabbit population almost wiped out by the myxomatosis epidemic of 1954. Scientists believe that the disappearance of the rabbit may have radically altered Britain's grassland habitat. No longer was there extensive heavy grazing by an abundance of rabbits. Grasses grew longer and provided more cover for hares, which helped them to erupt in numbers to a notable high between 1959 and 1962. This was followed by a number of very poor breeding seasons, and countrymen and sportsmen noticed a marked decline attributable to this

31 *A chequer-board pattern of arable farming, ideal for hares. They fare best where there is a diversity of crops, and where hedgerows and rough corners have not been totally removed in the interests of 'tidy' farming.*

alone. Apropos the interaction of rabbit and hare populations, it is also interesting to note that there are a number of accounts, as yet unsubstantiated by scientific evidence, of adult rabbits, especially old bucks, killing young leverets, apparently by biting at the head and neck.

Changing agricultural methods and the development of radically new arable cropping regimes have played a critical role in the decline of the hare by removing much of the traditional diversity of Britain's lowland farmland. A pattern of small fields with a diversity of crops, an abundance of rough and weedy corners, well established hedges, copses and woodland is ideal for hares, and the enlargement of field sizes, the removal of hedges and other cover, and the growing of large unbroken acreages of single crops have been largely responsible for the country-wide decline in hare numbers. 'Prairie farming' simply does not suit them; they fare much better in the sort of farmland evoked by the poet Gerard Manley Hopkins when he wrote of a 'landscape plotted and pieced, fold, fallow and plough'.

The third principal factor at work in this combination is fox predation. This is not similar in its timing and effects to the impact of hare shooting where the guns harvest a surplus in autumn and winter. By spring the fox's food requirements are high at a time when hares, like most game species, are only beginning to breed. Hares killed in early spring by foxes are a net loss to the total population and hare survival seems to be poorer in direct proportion to the abundance of foxes. Research work in Europe has revealed that where foxes have been reduced or eradicated by rabies control programmes hare populations have increased very significantly in subsequent years. But we still need to learn a great deal more about the interaction of foxes and hares in the British Isles.

The hare's breeding habits have been the subject of endless speculation and a wide range of conflicting views since the time of the earliest naturalists. Apart from those frequent medieval and Renaissance misunderstandings over the sex of individual hares, and claims that they were actually androgynous, it was only in modern times that biologists understood that female hares, like rabbits, can absorb their embryos, and that a pregnant hare can be mated and conceive a second time before she has given birth to her first leverets. Hares can breed in their first year and will reach physical maturity by the age of eight or nine months. Most females will produce three or four litters of young each year, with an interval of about two months between litters. The actual period of gestation is six weeks, and the three or four leverets in each litter are born with their eyes open, fully furred and capable of walking and moving about on their own if the need arises. But young leverets generally spend most of their time squatting, motionless and solitary, in a sheltered form quite apart from their mother and siblings.

This dispersal of young leverets is probably designed to

improve a hare family's chances of survival from predation. It is much better for the general survival of a hare family if only one leveret is caught and killed than if a fox should find and destroy an entire nest of three or four young. The mother will visit and suckle her young individually in their separate forms until they are fully weaned and capable of fending for themselves.

These are the secretive and usually unseen aspects of the hare's breeding biology, but much more conspicuous and dramatic are the courtship cavortings of hares in open fields in early spring. These are not only a familiar sight to the observant watcher but have been the subject of a great deal of description and of some excellent photography, both stills and movies. Spring and summer courtship among hares embraces a wide range of antics, including high-speed chases, dramatic leapings and boundings and, most extraordinarily comic of all, 'boxing matches', in which individuals stand erect and spar with one another using their forepaws. Contrary to belief about males fighting, this is almost always a non-receptive female repelling the advances of a male. From this behaviour evolved the folk tradition of the 'Mad March hare' – just one facet of the complex and many-sided mythology which has grown up around the hare, which enjoys a more elaborate and fascinating folklore than any other creature in the fauna of the British Isles.

12. *The Deer*

More than any other group of game species, deer represent the unbroken thread of continuity running through our sporting history and providing a link between today's sporting stalker or mounted huntsman and his counterparts of Norman times and before. The Saxons and earlier civilisations in Britain hunted deer for sport and meat, but it was the Norman conquest that brought in its wake a formalised system of laws and a highly ritualised approach to the sporting pursuit of deer. William of Normandy is generally credited with the founding of modern hunting, and it is the elaborate and harshly punitive Forest Laws enacted by him and his successors on the English throne that form the original basis of our modern system of game laws.

William I, 'who loved the tall red deer as if he were their father', wished to ensure the future of his sport and took two principal measures to bring this about. The royal forests were proclaimed reserves in which deer hunting was permitted only with the King's permission, with the death penalty for poaching. Extreme measures were also provided for anyone who harmed one of the King's hounds, the hideous fate of blinding with a red-hot poker being the statutory punishment. William's second measure was to extend the number of forests under royal control and to create new hunting preserves, of which the New Forest in south-west Hampshire was one of the most important. It was there that William's son and successor, William Rufus, a passionately enthusiastic sportsman, met his death while hunting in 1100, and the close association of royalty with hunting and field sports in general was to continue throughout medieval times, with a stream of legislation extending from the first proclamations of King Canute in the early eleventh century through Renaissance times up to the various post-war statutes enacted in these more democratic times by 'the Queen in Parliament' and including the vitally significant Deer Act of 1963, which forms the legislative and in many respects the philosophical foundation of deer control and sporting stalking today.

There are six species of deer at large and with well established feral populations in Britain today. The red deer (*Cervus elaphus*) and the roe (*Capreolus capreolus*) are native to Great Britain, both species having moved westwards across Europe and become established here before the land bridge with the continental mainland was broached. Roe never spread as far as Ireland before it became an island, but red deer had become firmly integrated into the Irish fauna, and residual populations linger in Killarney and perhaps still in parts of Wicklow, although hybridisation with sika and sika hybrids escaped from deer parks may have eroded the purity of the native strain of red deer there. The medieval English and Scottish monarchs relied upon red deer for their hunting, with the roe occupying a much more lowly position in their scale of values, and there was an interesting contrast between

32 The red deer is indigenous to the British Isles, although the original wild stock is now rare in Ireland. Here a stag roars in the rut on a Highland deer forest, where a smaller form of this large woodland species has adapted to life on the open hill. New afforestation programmes can bring deer and the forester into conflict.

the equally elaborate but otherwise very different styles of ritualised royal deer hunting in England and Scotland.

The English mode followed the Norman tradition of hunting on horseback with scenting hounds while the Scots coursed their deer with gazehounds, large, broken-coated deerhounds of the type immortalised in Ossianic legends and the pictures of Landseer. The Scottish approach was the *tainchell* or deer drive, a large-scale affair in which scores of beaters and dogs drove huge numbers of deer into gorges and blind valleys, where waiting marksmen took a massive toll of the deer. What deer did not fall to those primitive muskets and rifles were run down by teams of deerhounds in an orgy of slaughter which, while it provided diversion for the nobility, also fulfilled the more practical function of keeping their clansmen supplied with meat.

From the days of the royal stag hunt and the *tainchell* we have come a long way, to a point where the deer are now sporting quarry for the dedicated and usually solitary stalker with a highly accurate rifle, a precision tool which also plays a vital role in the management of deer populations, both for the good of the deer and to keep damage to trees and crops within acceptable limits.

Our two indigenous species of deer have been joined by the fallow (*Dama dama*), a species native to Mediterranean countries and perhaps first introduced by the Romans, with considerable further introductions during Norman times. Centuries were to pass before the arrival of another non-native deer, the sika (*Cervus nippon*), which came in various subspecific and racial forms from Japan, Manchuria and Taiwan. The first sika were brought to Ireland in the 1860s when the Viscount Powerscourt released them into his park in Wicklow. Some of their progeny and fresh stock from the Far East were released on properties in England and Scotland and for a time were much in vogue among Victorian 'acclimatisers' and deer enthusiasts. Muntjac (*Muntiacus reevesii*) were brought from south-east Asia around 1900 and the expansion of its feral populations since the early 1940s has been due to escapes from Woburn Park in Bedfordshire.

Today the 'jungle sheep' is widely distributed across the Midlands and Home Counties with signs of gradual expansion into Wessex.

The sixth species of deer, which gives Great Britain the largest number of feral deer species of any European country, is the Chinese water deer (*Hydropotes inermis*). These too escaped from captivity in the 1940s and have established a rather limited range in Bedfordshire and adjacent areas north of London and in parts of north-eastern East Anglia.

Deer are herbivorous, grazing on a wide range of grasses, heather, root crops, young cereals and many other types of ground vegetation, or browsing on brambles, ivy, shrubs and small trees. Their digestive system involves periods of eating followed by spells of rest and ruminative digestion – chewing the cud – similar to that of other ungulates like sheep, goats and cattle, to which deer are distantly related.

Deer, whatever their size, have virtually no means of physical defence against predators but rely upon their highly developed sensory awareness of imminent danger as a protection. Eyesight, though highly developed, is less acute in most deer than might be supposed and their eyes can often lack the resolving power to distinguish and identify as menacing a sombrely clad human figure standing still, even in open country. Their hearing, however, is very acute and the large and independently mobile ears tend to be continually on the move, picking up and locating the source of the slightest sounds. Most sensitive of all is the scenting ability of deer, which brings them a constant stream of information borne on the breeze. Any predator, human or animal, must make a stealthy upwind approach if it is to get close to deer. Agility and speed in flight, or an ability to melt soundlessly away into dense secondary growth, are their best protection when danger threatens.

Britain's native red deer and roe were formerly kept in check by natural predation. The wolf, the bear and the lynx were the principal carnivores that preyed upon our deer in ancient times, and a degree of natural balance was maintained. Human pressures and the need to protect domesti-

cated livestock led to the gradual extinction of all these large
carnivores in the British Isles, leaving weather, food and
habitat as the principal factors to limit deer numbers. Today
the only threat posed to deer by a wild carnivore is when
foxes take newly born or very weak fawns, as may occasionally happen, but otherwise man's activities have totally
removed the indigenous deer's natural enemies. Nor must
we forget the deliberate introduction of the four additional
non-native species already mentioned. All these feral
populations produce an annual crop of young and their
natural tendency is to increase in numbers until some factor,
or combination of factors, intervenes to set an upper limit.
Studies in Europe have shown that where lynx are present
they will predate heavily upon the roe deer in their hunting
range, taking the old and young, the diseased and those most
easily caught, and also exercising a more or less random
culling influence. When that local population has been
reduced to a level at which the lynx can no longer rely upon
roe as regular prey they will move on to fresh hunting
grounds and their predatory effects will be brought to bear on
another population. The remaining roe in the first area show
a capacity for rapid recovery in an environment where there
is no serious competition for habitat or food, and a healthy
and vigorous expansion in numbers results until the cycle is
complete and lynx predation begins again.

Man, having disrupted cycles of predation like this, now
bears the responsibility for managing deer and keeping their
numbers and the proportions of young to old and male to
female in balance. Two principal factors make this intervention essential. Deer which become too numerous will
overgraze their habitat and fall victim to starvation and
disease, some of which can be stress-related when real
overcrowding takes place. Intelligently planned deer management will include a cull to remove a surplus roughly
equivalent to the annual rate of increase, but taking into
account those deer which have died as the result of accidents
or disease. Deer populations maintained at optimum density
will be healthier and produce altogether finer specimens.

33 *A muntjac buck. This small, rather pig-like deer has spread widely across the Midlands and seems likely eventually to expand its range throughout southern England.*

Deer control is also vital because of the damage which they can and will do to the farmer's crops, the forester's trees and the gardener's shrubs and roses. Deer feed by grazing and browsing. Their tastes are catholic and include the leaves, shoots and bark of bushes and small trees; grasses, cereals and clover; and all types of vegetable and root crops. The more numerous the deer in relation to the availability of natural foods in their woodland and moorland habitats the worse their depredations upon commercial forests, farms and private gardens. If these essential rural and suburban activities are not to suffer intolerable damage, deer numbers must be kept in check.

To talk of culling deer is to invite two principal responses. Those who have seen their valuable arable crops and plantations of trees destroyed by deer will be understandably vengeful, and to them every dead deer may give cause for satisfaction. To others, primarily town dwellers, the very thought of shooting or in any way harming these elegant creatures with their Bambi associations seems unspeakable. Between these two entrenched and extreme views there lies a workable compromise – one which the deer themselves would vote for if they could.

Deer must be controlled and their numbers kept at a level which reduces damage to timber and other crops to a minimum while maintaining populations of healthy well-conditioned deer. We hold our two indigenous species in trust, if future generations are to enjoy our full heritage of native wildlife. As for the other four, we must face up to our responsibility for having brought them here. Vigorous, well managed populations of fallow, sika, muntjac and Chinese water deer are a pleasurable amenity and an economic asset, and one which deserves to be looked after, for ethical, aesthetic and economic reasons.

Contrary to the trends of most game species and other forms of wildlife in twentieth-century Britain, deer are flourishing and extending their range. It has been stated that there are now more deer in this country than in the days when Robin Hood and his contemporaries hunted them with their longbows of yew and arrows of ash – and risked incurring those barbarous punishments for infringing the Forest Laws. But Robin Hood was not a biologist and has left us no precise census data for deer populations in Norman times. Today, however, we can attempt a fairly accurate assessment based on data drawn from sporting estates, the Forestry Commission and a variety of other private and government sources. Scotland's population, composed primarily of red and roe deer, has been fairly accurately put at about 450,000; England and Wales probably add about half as many again, putting the total number of deer in Britain at close to three-quarters of a million, and that total is growing fast in many parts of the country.

The increased numbers of deer and the spread of their range are almost entirely due to afforestation. With the creation of the Forestry Commission in 1919 Britain

embarked upon a large-scale planting policy primarily
intended to rebuild the country's strategic timber reserves
which had been so severely depleted by the felling of half a
million acres or so as part of the war effort. In addition to
making good these wartime losses it was also intended to
reduce our timber imports, and thus improve our balance of
trade and create a greater degree of self-sufficiency in timber.
The resultant afforestation programme received particular
impetus after the loss of a similar acreage of woodland during
the Second World War. Since the 1950s vast acreages have
been planted for commercial timber production, especially in
the uplands and other areas where poor soils make land
generally unproductive for livestock or arable crops. Species
like Sitka and Norway spruce and lodgepole pine do well in
impoverished acidic soils which might otherwise only
sustain species like rowan, birch, willow, heather and upland
grasses such as bents and fescues. This is the sort of habitat
we chiefly associate with hill sheep farming and grouse
moors, but for a variety of reasons, some of which have been
discussed in the chapter on the red grouse, many such areas
have been ploughed and planted with fast-maturing
conifers, either at the instance of the Forestry Commission,
private forestry companies or individual landed proprietors.

The forester has usually been the chief ally of all our deer
species, although in practice he may actually feel more ill
disposed towards them than anyone. His planting activities
have provided deer with hundreds of thousands of acres of
cover and shelter, and the principal reservoirs of Britain's
deer populations are the large deciduous woods and small
game coverts of our lowland farming areas and the extensive
coniferous forests of northern England and Scotland. But deer
eat trees and their presence in woodland inevitably results in
some degree of damage to the trees, whether they are young
and recently planted or older and well established. Extreme
damage, such as the eating out of whole replanted areas or the
widespread fraying and peeling of bark on both young and
mature trees, can be so infuriating that the forester's reaction
is to organise a major pogrom against the offending animals.

This was especially true a generation ago, where new plantations were planned and laid out with no regard to the effects of deer on the new trees. New growth, or re-growth following clear-felling of old woods, provides browsing species like the roe with ideal conditions and they will thrive at the expense of the trees.

Today there is a rather more enlightened and informed climate of opinion in some forestry circles towards deer. At the very least foresters realise that, in most of Britain, forests and woods will harbour deer: that is a fact of life, and woodland management must take account of it and formulate forest designs and deer management strategies which will minimise the depredations of deer in commercial plantations. A more positive and constructive development is the emergence of a new breed of forester who, while still primarily concerned with the production of a crop of timber, also appreciates that wildlife, including deer, can be a real asset to woodland. Venison is excellent meat which is much in demand abroad and commands a high price. Sportsmen are willing to pay handsomely to stalk the better bucks and stags, and stalking charges and trophy fees can be another important source of income in addition to the venison sales. Deer are also a delightful amenity whose graceful and elegant appearance gives great pleasure to the public, especially the urban dweller who turns increasingly to the countryside for rest, relaxation and recreation. Those charged with the management of our forests, state-owned and private, have an increasing obligation to share them with others, so long as there is no undue conflict with their prime duty as timber producers. How does one put a price on the simple pleasure, so rare for a town dweller, of seeing wild deer in a bluebell-carpeted wood in spring? Only an incurable cynic – one who, in Oscar Wilde's phrase, 'knows the price of everything and the value of nothing' – could deny it.

For practical purposes most landowners, foresters, sportsmen and country-lovers in the British Isles will find that they encounter one or more of the four principal species – red deer, fallow, sika and roe – although the latter is absent from

Ireland and only beginning its westward colonisation of Wales. Chinese water deer are very localised in their distribution, and muntjac as yet represent a problem for the landowner or gardener only in a few heavily populated areas. The three biggest species – red, fallow and sika – prefer to feed by grazing rather than browsing, if the right herbage is available. They will also make destructive forays on to arable farmland, especially if this is bordered by woods in which they can lie up in the daytime. If adequate feeding for the deer is available within the woods they may not need to venture out much, if at all, but the critical time is late winter and spring, when grasses and other vegetation have died back and the farmers' stubble turnips or winter wheat may prove too tempting, especially for hungry does and hinds becoming heavier in fawn. In Scotland the red deer, formerly an animal of the great primeval Caledonian forests, has adapted with great success to a life on the open hill, where it grazes on upland grasses and heather. But severe winter weather drives the deer down to lower ground and each year there are instances of red deer marauding on farms and crofts, especially where root crops are grown. This makes them more than a little unpopular with the farmer, who is legally entitled to shoot them, regardless of the close seasons laid down by law, if he believes that serious crop damage can only be prevented by doing so. One must sympathise with the rage a crofter or farmer experiences on waking to discover that a crop has been ruined by an overnight deer raid. In Scotland many estates put out supplementary feed for their red deer in winter. This helps to sustain them through the leanest months of the year, to reduce winter mortality and maintain bodily condition until the 'early bite' and spring calving time arrives. Provision of hay, potatoes, swedes and other feedstuffs also reduces the likelihood of deer encroaching on farmland to find this food for themselves.

Fencing, of the correct height and design, can be very effective in keeping deer out – or in, depending upon your point of view. It is vital in certain circumstances, such as where young trees are being established in red deer country,

34 *Another introduced Asian species, the Sika deer, is now well established in parts of England and in areas of Ireland and Scotland. Like other deer they may encroach on farmland, and this hind and her yearling calf find a conventional sheep fence no obstacle to their movements on farmland in Ross-shire.*

but it is very expensive to surround any area, large or small, with a properly designed deer fence, which must be not less than 6 feet 4 inches high for red deer and about the same for sika and fallow. (The much smaller roe and muntjac can normally be excluded by a rather lower fence.) The larger the acreage planted and the larger the perimeter fence, the cheaper it becomes on a cost-per-acre basis. Nevertheless, it remains a very expensive business and is generally regarded as, at best, only 95 per cent effective. That remaining 5 per cent can make all the difference! All kinds of factors can conspire to make it possible for deer to get over or through the fence. Drifting snow against a fence can create a temporary ramp; a bank or hummock just outside the fence can give jumping deer a raised take-off point; floods, gales and associated problems such as windthrown trees collapsing across a fence will create gaps which deer seem to find with uncanny speed; and any inadequacies in the design or construction of fences will soon render them useless. If it really tries hard a red deer hind can squeeze through a vertical gap of only 7 inches, incredible though that may seem. The slender roe can push through almost any fence of horizontal wires, however tensely strung, and a mesh fence is really essential for deer of any species.

A great deal of afforestation and, to a lesser extent, the reclamation and enclosure of hill land for improved grazing or arable farming, has signally failed to take account of the needs and behaviour of deer. A forest which has been designed without regard to the well established, often age-old movements of deer in or through the area, where the plough driver has turned over every scrap of plantable land and the whole has finally been surrounded by a high perimeter fence – such an approach has often invited the deer damage which owners and managers have later deplored and made legitimate deer control difficult or impossible. They may have reacted to this situation by adopting a shoot-on-sight policy of deer control.

Red deer in Scotland have their regular patterns of summer dispersal, rutting assembly and the search of wintering shelter. If an area of sheltered lower ground, perhaps with a self-seeded growth of birches or willows giving additional natural cover, is suddenly ploughed, planted and fenced, the deer are deprived of their wintering refuge. The result will probably take one of two forms, both equally undesirable. Either the deer will be found dead, up against the fence in spring, or they will succeed in breaking into the forest, where tree damage from browsing, fraying and bark peeling may be very serious, even in well established plantations. Red deer previously accustomed to the slim pickings on the open hill will probably help themselves greedily to the plentiful feeding available in the forest but there will come a time when they will want to get out again on to the open hill. Driven mad by the insects in summer – especially by that supremely irritating little monster, the Highland midge –

their urgent desire is to escape to the breezy higher tops. Later, the rutting urge creates a similar need to break out. If this cannot be done easily the frustrated deer, especially mature stags, vent their feelings on the trees and so the damage to the forester's expensively established investment is compounded. This is a common picture in much of Scotland and the tell-tale signs are evident, with black peaty tracks worn round the insides of the perimeter fences by deer tramping round in search of a way out.

If red deer from the open hill have sufficient access to woodland they will become wedded or 'hefted' to it and will revert to being forest animals, as their ancient forebears were. Once they have become truly woodland animals they must be recognised and managed as such, and if this is done properly that harmonious balance between timber production, a healthy deer herd, a cash crop of venison and income from sporting fees may well be achieved. An acceptable level of damage to the trees is offset by income created by the presence of deer in the right numbers. That revenue is potentially high, for woodland red deer are larger, heavier specimens than their brothers on the hill. They make good bone, achieving high carcase weights, and grow bigger antlers in the more nutritious and mineral-rich environment of the woods. As sporting trophies they are much sought after, especially by Continental visitors; and heavier carcases in the deer larder naturally mean more income from venison sales. Mortality among woodland red deer of all ages is lower than on the hill, with better shelter from the Highland winter and more food of higher quality. Maturity comes sooner, too, and woodland hinds will produce their first calves at an earlier age than hill hinds. Productivity and calf survival is higher and this has obvious implications both for the management of red deer in Scottish forests and for the income which the venison and sporting fees can generate.

Sadly, this harmony which is so desirable is often not achieved. This is particularly true where some of the very large older forests, planned and planted perhaps thirty or more years ago, have become home for large populations of deer. Severe damage to mature trees, whatever form it takes, is very costly and, where the forest layout does not allow stalkers, professionals or paying visitors to cull the deer efficiently, desperate measures often result. This usually begins with a shoot-on-sight policy, where any deer of whatever age is shot, including hinds near to calving, hinds in milk which may leave unweaned orphaned calves, and promising stags in velvet. I vividly remember seeing the shooting of several magnificent adult stags, all with ten-point heads or better, still in velvet, in a forest in the west Highlands. They were shot from the cab of a Land Rover as they crossed a forest road on a sunny June afternoon – superb beasts, each of which could have commanded a premium trophy fee from a paying sportsman guest a couple of months later. But the forester had his orders and was struggling single-handed on 40,000 acres to control a population explosion of red deer. Every beast he shot, whatever the time of year, was one more to add to the cull total which his bosses had ordered him to get. It was a sorry sight, and one which distressed that particular forester too, but it is not an uncommon story in the Highlands, both in Forestry Commission and privately owned forests.

Frequent shooting and harassment in daytime makes deer very wary. They become increasingly nocturnal and the next stage in this 'crisis management' of deer is to implement a night shooting policy. Deer are 'lamped' with spotlamps or dazzled with vehicle headlights and shot quite indiscriminately, and no stalker, however skilful his marksmanship or woodcraft, will always kill every beast cleanly and recover all the carcases promptly on a pitch-black night in the depths of a conifer forest. Lamp shyness will eventually make even this form of control unworkable. This is the sort of lamentable situation which every enlightened forester, stalker, landowner and conservationist wishes to avoid. The answers are to seek better ways of effective deer control and the minimising of damage in our existing forests, and to design new forests so as to accommodate well regulated populations of deer within integrated forest policies. This is in many ways a

35 *Full tilt! A roe buck, antlerless in December, dashes past the guns on a pheasant shoot. Formerly roe were treated as vermin and shot indiscriminately with shotguns on deer drives. The stalker with a suitable rifle is now the most humane means of managing deer populations and taking a harvest of venison.*

microcosm of the challenge which faces game management in general, whatever the species. The search must be for ways of maintaining healthy, productive populations of game in a countryside which is also efficient in agricultural and silvicultural terms, and where the farmer, the forester, the stalker, the game shot, the rambler, the jogger and the dog-walker can each play his role without conflict.

Our deer management policies and activities in Britain and Ireland are currently undergoing a very exciting and important period of development and change. Former generations of professional stalkers and amateur enthusiasts refined and perfected the specialised techniques for stalking Scotland's unique Highland red deer on the open hill. But forty years ago there were only a handful of enthusiastic and knowledgeable woodland deerstalkers. In every aspect of woodland deer management and sporting stalking our European neighbours, especially in Germany and Scandinavia, were streets ahead of us. The period of occupation after the last war gave stalking-minded servicemen many opportunities for studying and participating in European woodland deer control and there began a major revolution in British stalking attitudes.

Roe deer in Britain have only recently come to prominence as a quarry for the sporting stalker. Apart from a small number of dedicated enthusiasts – names like Frank Wallace and J. G. Millais spring to mind at once – no one bothered to stalk roe with a rifle. Usually they were dismissed as vermin, shot indiscriminately and frequently only wounded on pheasant drives, snared in commercial woodlands and on farmland and accorded a negligible sporting status. Ironic-ally, the shotgunners' deer drives of the 1940s and 1950s which were intended to wipe out roe actually played an important part in encouraging their spread, especially in southern England. Today it is the solitary stalker with his rifle, usually of modern, flat-trajectory calibre and with a telescopic sight, which makes possible accurate shooting in the poor light of early dawn and late dusk, who is the effective deer manager.

In woods and on arable farmland deer control requires much more than merely the possession of a suitable rifle and the ability to use it accurately. The stalker must be very familiar with his ground and the deer which live there, and have a grasp of the biological principles upon which effective deer management is based. Like anyone involved in the husbandry of any population of game or other wildlife, he can only proceed if his practical measures are well founded on a thorough understanding of the natural history of the species concerned. The stalker must also adopt a pragmatic and open-minded attitude to his task. The individual cir-cumstances which prevail in one area may dictate a quite different approach from that which would be best in another. There is little room for rigid dogma in the business of deer management in the rapidly changing environment of Britain today. We have some striking object lessons showing how in other countries an inflexible and doctrinaire strategy of deer control has failed, resulting in poorer physical specimens and the inefficient deployment of manpower and resources. West Germany provides a notable example of a strictly defined roe deer management policy, followed almost slavishly since its inception in the 1930s. The roe deer of Germany in the 1980s are generally smaller and poorer beasts than our British roe, despite (and, many would say, because of) decades of selective culling in conformity with well established principles. It is ironic to see how many German and other European roe enthusiasts now come to Britain, often at considerable expense, to stalk the trophy quality roebucks which are so few and far between in their home countries.

A sound ground rule in the management of roe and other woodland deer is the establishment and maintenance of a stable ratio of males to females and old to young. The birth rate and survival success of the deer in any given area must be constantly monitored and a crop of surplus animals culled so as either to maintain stability or to reduce or, sometimes, expand the deer population, depending upon the demands and constraints of farming, forestry, the landowner's requirements and the instructions the stalker is given. One of the best things to happen in the deer world in the post-war period is the emergence of a new breed of stalkers, who are developing skills and knowledge in woodland deer management, derived in many respects from the European tradition but suitably modified to suit the British situation. The British Deer Society, the St Hubert Club of Great Britain and the Game Conservancy have all played important roles in promoting a new, soundly based approach to deer management and in training many of the growing band of enthusiastic amateurs and dedicated professionals upon whom the informed management of our deer increasingly depends.

Like Britain, Ireland too has growing numbers of deer, although only three wild and feral species are involved. The indigenous red deer, once very seriously depleted and localised in their distribution, have been augmented by escapes from deer parks, and together with the introduced fallow and sika have expanded considerably, benefiting from the large areas of the Irish Republic and Northern Ireland which have recently been afforested with conifers.

Sadly but not surprisingly the security situation in Ireland has severely restricted private ownership of suitable rifles for deerstalking, with centre-fire rifles almost unobtainable in Northern Ireland and the stalker in the Republic currently permitted nothing larger than ·22 centre-fire calibres like the ·22–250 Remington and the 5·6 × 57 mm. Irish deerstalkers are only too conscious of the inadequacy of the tools they are forced to use and their concern and enthusiasm for the welfare of Ireland's deer is all the greater. The Irish Deer Society, various groups of keen stalkers and some enlightened foresters have fought long and hard to get a better deal for deer throughout Ireland, and the Republic's legislation in 1976 and the Northern Ireland Wildlife Order 1985 have provided important new safeguards for deer, thanks in large measure to years of lobbying and pressure from deer-minded Irish sportsmen. Their enthusiasm, knowledge and expertise will become all the more important if, as seems likely, deer continue to spread and colonise new areas of forest. The inevitable conflict between uncontrolled deer and vulnerable tree crops has been evident in many areas of Ireland for some time and is unlikely to diminish unless skilled stalkers are permitted to get to grips with the situation. The alternative is that deer populations will get out of control in some areas, and both the timber crop and the deer will ultimately suffer.

Stalkers, professional and amateur, can do their best work towards achieving a harmony between deer, trees and farming only if the deer can be adequately studied, counted and culled throughout the rotation of the forest crops. With existing forests the layout of the trees and the pattern of clear-felling, windthrow, clearance and replanting will largely dictate the response of deer to this changing environment and the extent to which the stalker can manage them effectively. New forests, however, are another matter.

Prevention is better than cure and this is as true of deer

damage as any other problem. If a new forest or plantation can be designed and laid out taking deer into account the problem need never arise. The key principle is that the forest design must enable the stalker to control the deer at all stages in the development of the forest.

Solid blocks of forest divided by relatively narrow rides or firebreaks are almost certain to harbour deer in larger numbers than the trees can stand and the stalker may find himself unable to tackle his management task properly. Gaps, clearings, natural open avenues like the course of a stream, wider rides and forest roads with unplanted verges all give the deer access to areas where they can enjoy the warmth of direct sunlight and feed on the vegetation along the forest edge. Here too, when deer are visible in the open, are the spots for the observation, counting and culling of deer. And in considering the multiple use of afforested land it is important to remember the amenity value of providing areas where the public can have the chance to see deer, and where the visiting enthusiast can sketch or photograph wild deer. Forests which are not unduly regimented in their layout are so much more pleasing to the eye than geometrically planted stands of even-aged monoculture marching in straight, evenly spaced ranks across the countryside, making no concessions to the land's contours and other natural features. Wildlife conservation benefits greatly from a more flexible and imaginative approach to forest design, and such a forest will fulfil many other useful roles in addition to its primary purpose of producing a timber crop.

Deer, like most game birds and mammals in woodland, enjoy clearings where the sun can get through the canopy of trees and warm the forest floor; they visit them frequently. If small areas, perhaps only two or three acres in roe areas, can be left unplanted they will usually prove to have a magnetic attraction for deer.

Species like birch, willow, ash and various low-growing shrubs can be planted and encouraged along the edge of the main timber crop and will relieve browsing and fraying pressure. Such glades, or 'deer lawns', should prove attrac-

36 *A Bambi-like roe kid, one of twins found in a Hampshire woodland in May. Roe are rapid and prolific breeders and their numbers must be carefully regulated to maintain a balance between flourishing populations of healthy deer and an acceptably low level of damage to trees and crops.*

tive to deer for the warmth, shelter and feeding they offer. They not only reduce the damage done by deer to the growing timber but also enable the stalker to see his deer and cull them properly. Depending upon the lie of the land and the access tracks, such glades can either be stalked on foot or a high seat can be sited there. High seats, if they are thoughtfully sited and well built, can have a long, useful life and are an important aid to deer culling. They also make excellent platforms for the general observation and photography of woodland wildlife.

In planning a new forest attention should also be paid to areas which are likely to attract deer and which may also be less suitable for planting. Warm, sheltered south-facing slopes may be very attractive to deer, and if they are rocky or very steep, or if the soil type is poor, they may never be really

satisfactory for growing trees. If these and other unfavourable forestry areas, such as frost pockets, are left unplanted
the forester avoids wasting his time trying to establish trees
in unsuitable spots and leaves them as natural deer haunts
where the stalker can see and cull his selected beasts. Streams
should also be left with wide unplanted margins, to encourage deer to feed along the side where they can be seen,
and such watercourses give the stalker natural paths along
which to spy and stalk his deer. Recent studies on the
acidifying effects of conifers planted close to hill burns and
the headwaters of salmon and trout rivers also indicate that
the trees should be kept well back from the water's edge, as
discussed in the chapter on game fish. This is another good
reason for resisting the temptation to plough and plant right
up to the banks.

Trees like Sitka spruce grow fast – that is why they are
planted – and the appearance of a forest changes rapidly
within a few years. What may seem to be a generously wide
ride or firebreak in the early years may grow in and look very
narrow as the trees mature. Imaginative forest planning
should envisage how such breaks and gaps will look
throughout the life of the forest and appropriate action
should be taken to give the stalker and the deer the open
spaces they need. Thought must also be given to the logistical
problems of getting the carcases of large deer like red stags
out of a forest and down to the game larder. No one who has
not had to tackle the job of getting an eighteen-stone stag
carcase out of deeply ploughed furrows and drains and
through solid plantations to the nearest vehicle access point
can imagine what a backbreaking struggle it is!

With the increasing and legitimate demand for public
access to the countryside and its woodlands, for recreation
and leisure use, this too must be considered in planning a
forest and the management of the deer which will live in it.
Human disturbance will upset the deer and may cause an
increase in the amount of damage they do, and also make
them very difficult to stalk. Early-morning joggers and
courting couples at dusk will add to the general level of

disturbance caused throughout the rest of the day by dog-walkers and casual strollers, in addition to any forestry operations which may be in progress. Careful planning and signposting of forest walks, paths and nature trails and the judicious siting of car parks and picnic areas can help to guide visitors into those areas of the forest where they will cause minimum disruption to wildlife in general and to any shooting which may be going on. Ramblers and joggers will upset the deer, while a man in camouflaged clothing emerging out of the dusk of a summer's evening carrying a rifle and a freshly gralloched deer carcase will most assuredly upset any courting couple he meets! Discreet mutual avoidance prevents such problems from arising.

It is not being negative to think in these ways about the culling and commercial stalking of our deer. Their numbers are growing, their local populations must be controlled for their own good and to avoid serious conflict with forestry and farming, and the woodlands which harbour deer must have regard to the basic requirements of deer and of the stalker charged with managing them. The competent and knowledgeable rifleman is the only efficient predator we now have and the burden for caring for the welfare of our deer falls upon him. His effectiveness depends upon a wider acceptance of the need for a modern approach to deer management, based upon a sound understanding of the species and their ways. The alternatives, such as indiscriminate shotgunning of marauding deer, high mortality through winter starvation and the abominable last resort of poisoning to control excessive deer populations, are repugnant to sportsmen and to all who love these most elegant of creatures.

13. *The Game Fish*

'Game fish', to most anglers, invariably means salmon, brown trout and sea trout. Others would maintain that the term should be taken as embracing all the salmonid species, that extended family of freshwater and migratory fishes of which we regard the salmon as head, and which also includes grayling, char, pollan, vendace and powan (also known locally as schelly or gwyniad). In reality the game fisherman's activities and the management of game fisheries in the British Isles depend almost exclusively upon our native salmon, sea trout and brown trout, to which must be added the introduced 'exotic' rainbow trout, which plays an increasingly important role in providing game fishing in many parts of Britain, and chiefly on stillwaters.

   This chapter is not intended to be an exhaustive discussion

of all or indeed any of these salmonid species. A vast and growing literature on them already exists, and the intention here is to consider some aspects of the current status and future prospects for the survival of our more familiar game fish. It is not within the scope of this book to attempt more than an assessment of the present position and the future outlook for our commonest and most widespread species of game fish. They deserve a place in any general discussion of game; they have a very substantial sporting and economic importance; and they play an especially important role as indicators of the many radical and destructive changes which man has wrought in the environment.

Salmon, sea trout and brown trout are closely related – both biologically and in the mind of the sportsman – as members of a sub-order of fishes, all of which can be distinguished by the distinctive adipose fin, the small secondary dorsal fin lying to the rear of the much larger main dorsal fin. The fish of the Salmonoidei sub-order are either freshwater, marine or 'anadromous' – that is, breeding in fresh water and migrating to feed at sea. The British marine representatives of the purely sea-living species are called 'argentines' and are occasionally caught by commercial sea fishermen in the deep waters off the west and south west of Ireland where the European continental shelf drops away into the ocean depths. How many people have ever even heard of a fish called an argentine?

Much more familiar and important are the brown trout (*Salmo trutta*), which lives entirely in freshwater, and the Atlantic salmon *(Salmo salar)*, which hatches and develops in fresh water before migrating to the sea, from which it returns for the sole purpose of breeding. The sea trout, sometimes formerly known as *Salmo fario*, is now accepted as a migratory or anadromous form of *Salmo trutta*, that is, it is the same basic species as the brown trout. It occupies a niche between the other two, being apparently less well adapted than the salmon to life in the sea but more like the brown trout in that it feeds regularly in fresh water and will return from the sea without spawning. In the sea they do not venture so far afield and often remain around estuaries for long periods, making earlier and more frequent returns to the rivers. Compared with salmon, sea trout seem better adapted to brackish conditions, and it is interesting to note that in the less salty waters of the Baltic Sea they are known to achieve weights of up to 50 pounds, while salmon are rarely more than 20 pounds. The brown trout is now regarded simply as a variety of *S. trutta* which lacks the urge to migrate to sea, although it may make freshwater migrations, moving upstream to spawn or migrating from lakes into the inflowing rivers and streams at spawning time.

If these closely related fish had a common ancestor from which they evolved, was it a freshwater fish or a sea fish? You could fill a library with the books and learned papers written about the salmon family, all evidence of the historical fascination and great economic importance of these fish, and still this basic question has not been conclusively answered. Perhaps the answer involves a compromise, and the ancestral species was an estuary dweller, feeding and breeding in brackish water: one Pacific salmon species, the pink or humpbacked salmon *(Oncorhynchus gorbuscha)* is known to do this. But our concern is with the Atlantic salmon and the sedentary and migratory forms of *S. trutta* which, whatever their evolutionary origins, all breed in our freshwater rivers and provide a quality of sport and generate a measure of income and employment which we cannot ignore. Not least, their fortunes and the relative abundance of their populations are a telling reflection of the ecological well-being of our rivers and lakes, and of the environment of the British Isles as a whole.

Our ancestors, whether amateur enthusiasts or professional biologists, delighted in noting and classifying all the many varieties of trout and game fish and concocted a quite bewildering range of trout 'species' to account for the variations of colour, size and general appearance which they saw. Who can blame them? My own thoughts immediately go to one small area in the west of Ireland where three loughs, all within easy walking distance of each other, produce brown

37 *A salmon leaping the falls on its upstream spawning run. Salmon were once abundant in rivers like the Thames, the Severn and the Mersey, but pollution, degradation of their river spawning habitat and over-exploitation at sea have reduced Britain's salmon stocks to a fraction of their former levels.*

trout which look so different from each other that one might
well be dealing with three separate species. The fish in one
are small and dark, with blackish fins and blood-red spots,
and anything over six ounces is a monster. Less than a mile
away another lough yields trout whose typical style is a
uniform buttery gold with only the most muted speckling,
and growing up to 3 pounds or more. The third holds trout of
a dullish silvery-brown, heavily marked with black and pink
spots. With brown trout we are in fact dealing with a species
which is enormously variable and whose members adapt,
genetically and in behaviour, to cope with differences which
include such matters as geology, alkaline or acid water, types
and availability of food, and many other factors. All healthy
individuals will interbreed and produce fertile offspring,
which fulfils the biologists' standard definition of a species –
the European trout, *Salmo trutta*. The Atlantic salmon, by
contrast, is uniform in appearance throughout its range.

Fish of the salmon family have become an increasingly
important indicator of the purity of freshwater river systems.
The former abundance of salmon in rivers like the Tyne (once
England's most prolific salmon river), the Trent, the Mersey,
the Medway and the Thames is in bleak contrast to the
present state of those rivers. While the Tyne has never
altogether lost its game fish, despite the worst effects of
industrialisation and the pollution which has accompanied
it, rivers like the Mersey and the Thames became so heavily
polluted and their flow so disrupted by weirs, locks and other
barriers to migratory fish that salmon vanished altogether.
With the rapid expansion of London and its population from
the mid-eighteenth century onwards and the mushroom
development of the cities of the Industrial Revolution like
Liverpool, Glasgow, Manchester and Belfast, effluents, general
water pollution and the effects of obstruction and diversion
of water flow virtually wiped out salmon and trout stocks. In
many of the old by-laws and municipal records of these
industrial cities there is evidence of the former superabundance of salmon, usually in the form of some limitation of the
extent to which each city's indented apprentices could be fed

on fresh salmon. In many cases this was by far the cheapest and most readily available meat in the late eighteenth and early nineteenth centuries, and parsimonious tradesmen inevitably tended to choose the cheapest way of maintaining their apprentices, for whose board and lodging they were responsible. A general compromise seems to have evolved whereby apprentices were not to be fed fresh salmon more than three days each week. Think of that in terms of the Mersey, the Humber or the Clyde in the 1980s – or, in the wider European context, of the Rhine, once the premier salmon river of northern Europe and now its largest sewer.

It is only realistic to recognise that in most of Britain's rivers draining industrial areas salmon and trout have virtually gone for ever. However strenuous the efforts of water authorities to achieve lower pollution levels and to provide passes and fish ladders for salmon and sea trout, rivers like the Trent, the Medway, the Ouse and others will never again support worthwhile populations of game fish. The best we can hope for is the reduction of pollution and a general improvement in river management to a point where some trout and a marginal salmon population may be able to hang on. That will at least be a step forward for the filthy rivers we have inherited and may help salve the consciences of industrialists, water authorities and government departments. It will most assuredly not restore what has otherwise been so utterly destroyed.

It is not as if our industrial, filth-creating forebears had not been warned of the likely consequences of their activities. Over five centuries ago the Irish took one of the first local legislation measures when, in 1466, Dublin Corporation banned the city's flourishing leather trade from using the salmon-rich waters of the Liffey for washing or treating any leather or manufactured material containing lime. This was an important new departure, earlier legislation having been chiefly concerned not with the insidious effects of pollution but with the more overt and calculated abuse of nets, fish traps, poisons and other methods of taking salmon, especially during the close season. In 1030 Malcolm II, King of Scotland, enacted close season legislation for the period from late August to mid-November, while English statutes of the thirteenth and fourteenth centuries also showed the Crown's solicitude for the well-being of inland fisheries by establishing close seasons and providing severe financial and custodial penalties for the illegal taking of fish or the obstruction of running fish. But frequent subsequent legislation and constant concern expressed at all levels about the purity of our river systems and the state of their game fish populations have been largely ineffectual. At best they may have slowed the rate of destruction of our rivers and lakes, but the trout and salmon populations of much of Britain and Ireland have been in steady and relentless retreat for two centuries and more.

If you mention salmon to the sportsman of the 1980s his thoughts will almost certainly turn to Scotland. There, in the great east-coast river catchments like Tweed, Tay, Dee and Spey, and in countless smaller spate rivers in the west Highlands and the Isles, are the last bastions of Britain's salmon. That is not to deny the existence of salmon in other waters, such as the chalk streams of the south of England and the spate rivers of the West Country, Wales and Ireland, but they are numerically insignificant by comparison with Scotland's salmon. No one can deny the magnificence of the heavy, well made salmon of the Hampshire Avon, for example, but how long will they survive the effects of agrochemicals leaching into the river systems, the increasing nitrate and phosphate content of the water, and all the pressures of the human population and the resulting degradation of the river habitat? The Welsh and West Country river systems are, in general, short and often comparable to many of the west Highland and western Irish rivers. Their importance for the future of salmon in the British Isles although it is not insignificant is not to be compared with that of, for example, the Tay, 116 miles long and with a catchment area which comprises some 3,000 square miles, a vast share of Scotland's land area. It is on the river systems of Scotland, large and small, from the Borders through the Highlands to

Orkney, Shetland and westwards into the Hebrides, that the real battle to save Britain's salmon is now being fought. For this reason much of what follows will concentrate on Scotland and the problems currently facing its environment in general and its game fish in particular.

Scotland's salmon fisheries, for which regulating laws can be traced back almost a thousand years, are today largely governed by legislation enacted in 1862, 1864 and 1868. Subsequent amendments and supplementary provisions have done little to update the law and Britain's greatest twentieth-century salmon fisheries are still regulated by what are essentially nineteenth-century laws. This is an astonishing indictment of successive governments for failing to keep abreast of the situation. The 1868 Act was, in its day, a fine piece of work and a credit to the intelligent foresight of those who wanted to ensure a future for Scotland's fisheries. With the passage of the 1868 Act Scotland's salmon enjoyed better protection than those of England, Wales or Ireland, but legislation must keep abreast of changes in land use, population, pollution and many other factors if it is to continue to be useful. Fisheries legislation has largely failed to do this.

Scotland, more than any other part of Great Britain, has undergone very radical changes over the past century. The legislators of mid-Victorian times were dealing with a country only recently made readily accessible to visitors by the expansion of the new railway system. The salmon rivers attracted the sportsman, as did the grouse and deer on the hills, and there was a relatively stable relationship between the sporting interests and the traditional practices of low-intensity hill sheep farming and a predominantly crofting style of agriculture. Today the Highland and Borders landscapes have been utterly transformed, chiefly by the afforestation of millions of upland acres.

Afforestation with conifers had been undertaken by various private proprietors on their Scottish estates since the eighteenth century, and it was planting of this sort which enabled Sir Thomas Fowell Buxton and Lord Breadalbane successfully to re-establish the capercaillie in east Perthshire in the 1830s.

But with the creation of the Forestry Commission and an upsurge of government-backed afforestation activity after the First World War there began a new process which still continues and which has brought major and often detrimental changes to Scotland.

Self-sufficiency in timber is the rainbow which has been chased by foresters ever since the Forestry Act of 1919 set up the Forestry Commission. 450,000 acres of trees were felled in the years 1914–18 as part of the war effort and a slightly larger acreage was to follow in 1939–45. Britain, then as now, had to import most of the timber it needed, and it was felt desirable to grow more timber of our own. From a simple balance of payments viewpoint this seems a sensible policy, and the mild, humid climate and the acidic, peaty soils of the uplands were seen as ideal for the growing of species like Sitka spruce, whose natural habitat is the shallow peaty soil and oceanic climate of British Columbia. A big timber crop will, it is argued, reduce the need for imports while providing employment in deprived upland areas where there might otherwise be few jobs.

But what have Scotland's new forests to do with salmon and trout? In broad terms there are two effects – drainage, and the chemical and mineral impact on the environment. The foresters' deep ploughing and the creation of networks of drainage channels have quite changed the way in which rainfall eventually finds its way into streams, rivers and lakes, and its acidity and chemical make-up when it gets there. Where once rainwater filtered slowly through blanket peat and moorland soils and eventually seeped into the burns and so into the general river systems, it now runs off the land much faster, causing rapid rises and drops in water levels and rates of flow. Comparatively little rain is now sufficient to cause spate conditions in some rivers where previously this only happened after substantial cloudbursts or prolonged and very heavy rain. Fast-flowing water in forestry drainage channels has an eroding effect which can lead to the silting up of the gravel spawning beds of trout and salmon, as peat, soil and other debris are washed away and carried downstream.

38 *This sea-trout, a migratory form of the brown trout (Salmo trutta) is making violent sideways movements with her tail and body to cut a spawning redd for her eggs in the clean gravel at the headwaters of the river. Silting up of the gravel can destroy the spawning grounds of salmon and trout and seriously reduce their numbers.*

Spate conditions result in a loss of bank vegetation, making the burn banks unstable and more liable to cave in, and insect and invertebrate life is also lost. Really violent spates can disturb and dislodge the gravel of the spawning beds, destroying the buried eggs of trout and salmon, but a greater and more general threat is the silting up and compacting of river beds where formerly water percolated, freely and well oxygenated, through the gravel.

Spawning trout and salmon use vigorous tail and body movements to create eddies which wash the gravel into hollows. This essential cutting of the spawning redds is impossible if clay, silt and other matter has caused infilling and compacting of the gravel. Faster run-off and frequent violent fluctuations in the flow rate and water level create an unstable and unnatural river environment. Game fish ova are normally buried sufficiently deeply in the gravel to be unaffected by spates, but the silting and compacting caused by the effects of afforestation upon drainage create other problems. Salmon and trout select spawning areas where water currents along the bed of the stream flow through the gravel. Silt and other debris tends to be deposited on the upstream surface of mounds and bars of gravel, leaving the water to filter through and emerge on the downstream side, carrying away any silt deposits from that area. This enables the ova in the spawning redds, which are nothing more than fish-created humps and mounds of gravel, to enjoy a flow of well filtered water. In this way spawning redds can cope with a certain amount of mud and silt, but a point can be reached where the rate of deposition, compacting and contamination of the habitat of the ova is faster than the currents can cope with. This marks the point at which the environment of the river goes into decline, and the game fish with it.

While this is a very real problem in Scotland's river systems where the headwaters and spawning areas are increasingly surrounded by conifer afforestation, the damaging effects of silting, compacting and waste deposition are also to be seen in the lowland river systems. The late Frank Sawyer, doyen of chalkstream fishery managers, wrote and broadcast about these problems and how they had progressively inhibited and eventually destroyed natural spawning by trout in stretches of the Hampshire Avon and other south-country rivers. He particularly condemned the build-up of sludge and river-bottom acidity where decaying leaves from deciduous bankside trees had fallen into the river. He also noted that insects in the dun and spinner stage will not be palatable food for fish if they have developed from larvae emerging from a dirty or silted-up river bed. In the spawning stretches of Scotland's rivers this deciduous riparian growth is not generally present, but the non-native evergreen conifers can pose their own problems. The shading effect of stands of mature conifer can inhibit insect and invertebrate life along upland streams, and a recent survey clearly illustrated the extent of the conifer problem. Open moorland streams were compared with those which drain mature plantations of conifers. In the study area in central Scotland almost all the forest streams held no trout: open moorland burns invariably held good numbers of game fish. Why does afforestation with conifers have this drastic effect? Drainage is only one contributory factor; mineral and chemical influences also play their destructive part.

'Acid rain' has been a much discussed phenomenon throughout Europe since the 1970s, although the term is rather misleading. The acidity of the actual rain which falls is only one aspect of the larger, more serious and infinitely more complicated problem of general acid deposition and the progressive acidification of the environment. Afforestation, the nature of the conifer vegetation and the accompanying changes in drainage and faster water run-off all contribute to this problem.

The acid or alkaline state of water is expressed as a pH value, a concept familiar to farmers, gardeners and anyone who ever studied elementary chemistry at school. The higher the number, the more alkaline the conditions. The 'natural' pH of rainfall over the British Isles is 5·6, a slightly acid solution of water with atmospheric carbon dioxide. This marginally acid rain falls to earth and as it soaks away, draining and percolating through vegetation, soil, peat and rocks, its acidity is changed. An alkaline environment will reduce the natural acidity of rain, and the water which eventually drains into rivers and lakes may be much more alkaline as the result of absorbing alkaline substances. The richest plant, insect and invertebrate life is found in relatively alkaline waters, and this abundance of food items promotes the growth and condition of fish. Acid water and a more meagre diet account for the smaller trout of upland streams and lochs compared with those of the food-rich south-country chalk streams and the limestone loughs of Ireland. However, the acidity of

39 *These mayflies, like many other forms of waterside insects, are a favourite food of trout, which will eat them eagerly in the nymph, emergent and spent stages of their life cycle. But they are unpalatable to fish if they have hatched from a river or lake bed which is silted up and dirty.*

Scotland's river systems is often not being reduced by any de-acidifying action of vegetation and geology. Instead it is becoming more acidic, and more hostile to game fish, for two principal reasons. Acidity at a pH level below 4·5 is regarded as lethal to game fish ova and to fish at the alevin stage, when the young trout and salmon have hatched and begun to develop in the river-bottom gravels. Acidic conditions also disrupt the normal breeding activity of fish and upset the working of the gills and the fish's respiratory system. The needles which fall from coniferous trees acidify the ground, and the water which seeps through it, as this forest litter decomposes. Other acidic matter leaches out of the ground, and forests 'store' large amounts of water in the trees, and this abstraction of water results in a concentration of acidic elements and a shift away from the acid-neutralising effects of calcium in the environment and towards the acid-promoting influence of the hydrogen ion.

Trees also have a very much larger surface area than moorland vegetation such as heather and grasses. This may enable them to collect acidity from rainfall more effectively than the plants which were there before. But this is made worse by the increasing acidity of the rainfall over Scotland. Human pressures and especially the demand for electricity have produced high levels of oxides of nitrogen and sulphur in the atmosphere, chiefly as a result of the burning of the so-called fossil fuels – coal, oil and other petroleum derivatives. These acidic oxides are washed out of the air in solution with the rainwater and the result is an increasingly acidic rainfall. Against the 'natural' rainwater pH of 5·6 mentioned earlier, the rainfall of north-west Scotland now averages about 5·0. A band across south-western, central and north-eastern Scotland has a rainfall of between 4·3 and 4·6. South-eastern Scotland has quite the most acidic rainfall, estimated at pH 4·0-4·3.

This pattern is believed to reflect the oxide emissions from sources in industrial areas of mainland Europe which have their greatest impact on the rainfall over southern and eastern Scotland. The geology of south-eastern Scotland is largely able to mitigate and neutralise this very acidic rainfall as the water percolates through the more alkaline soils and rocks of that area. Consequently the water which eventually flows into the lochs and rivers is much less acidic and thus not a significant risk to game fish and other river life.

It is a different story elsewhere in Scotland. The impact of acidic rainfall is worst in areas where the soils are already acidic and peaty, usually where the underlying rock is granite, schist or quartzite. Catchment areas like these cannot de-acidify the rainwater, and these are the very areas where conifer afforestation is most widespread. Large tracts of the Highlands and south-west Scotland are already ploughed and planted, and tens of thousands of acres will follow in the future. A more acidic rainfall and a style of forestry which adds further to that acidity spells the ruination of many fisheries. Not only does the acid quality of the water militate against ova and alevin survival, and the availability of invertebrate food for fish, but acidity promotes the leaching of certain metal ions from the soil and rocks. Aluminium in particular is highly toxic even to adult salmon and trout in waters where the acidity is high (pH 4·5–5·5); it prevents the normal absorption of oxygen, sodium and calcium.

These, in brief outline, are some of the environmental changes which are already threatening Scotland's game fish, both resident trout and migratory salmon and sea trout. In particular afforestation has a great deal to answer for, and its contribution to the acidification of the environment and the drainage patterns of river catchments may have consequences which extend far beyond fish alone. At the simplest level of human response, these blankets of green have destroyed the once-lovely face of large areas of Scotland – and of the uplands elsewhere in Britain and Ireland too. The new commercial monoculture forests are not things of beauty. Tourists find them ugly and generally avoid them, and they have destroyed large areas of upland habitat where once the trout, the grouse and many other upland species used to abound. Despite the enlightened approach of some private proprietors and forestry companies who have planned their forest with the interests of wildlife, water systems and the general environment in mind, most of our large-scale ploughing and planting has been ineptly planned and thoughtlessly laid out. Its environmental consequences are serious, and what has been done, much of it with the backing of public funds and taxpayers' money, is viewed by many environmentalists as major national scandal.

Afforestation, acidification and associated matters are by no means the only threats facing Britain's populations of game fish. In particular migratory fish like salmon and sea trout are faced with many additional hazards, as they move up and down the rivers and also when they are in the open sea, which do not apply to the more sedentary freshwater brown trout. But both resident and migratory trout and salmon must first survive their early days in the rivers which may not always be a safe nursery for them. It is worth considering their life-cycle briefly, and the survival risks to which they are exposed.

Salmon and sea trout must have access to freshwater river systems in which to spawn and so perpetuate the species. But the growth of the individual fish depends upon its feeding activities at sea. Salmon do not feed at all in fresh water: sea trout will do so, but we have already noted how the migratory S. trutta occupies a niche between the brown trout of fresh water and the highly sea-adapted salmon, whose sole purpose in leaving the sea for freshwater is to spawn. Both anadromous fish migrate to sea after their early period of development in the river. The ova hatch in the gravel of the redds after a period which is dictated by the water temperature, with earlier hatching in warmer water. An average temperature of 2°C will result in salmon ova hatching after about 115 days, with sea trout taking considerably longer at about 148 days, as for brown trout – and this will be the case in river systems where the spawning streams are in exposed high-altitude areas where water temperatures are low in winter and early spring. An average of 7°C, however, will reverse the situation, with salmon ova hatching after some 90 days and sea trout and brown trout noticeably earlier at 68 days.

After enzyme action has dissolved the egg membranes and the young fish has broken its way out it enters the alevin stage of its life, a small creature perhaps half an inch long and equipped with its own food supply in the form of a yolk-sac. Young alevins remain in the safety of the gravel where they grow relatively quickly, and they will have doubled their length to an inch or so by the time the yolk-sac's contents are exhausted and the sac has been absorbed. Water temperature will affect the rate of the alevin's development but within two or three weeks of hatching the young fish will have entered the fry stage of its life. At this point young fish will be identifiable as salmonids by a red tinge on the edge of the adipose fin in the case of trout and, more obviously, by the 'parr marks' on the flanks of both species – large dark upright bars often compared in appearance to thumb-prints.

Fry, of whatever species, are territorial in their behaviour, usually lying in shallow water and spaced several inches apart, each living and feeding within its own small home range. In a familiar survival-of-the-fittest manner the keenest feeders will grow fastest, holding the best territories and gaining size and weight more quickly than others. Some fry seem never to learn to feed properly at all and die shortly after the alevin stage. After the first year of life, trout and sea trout fry will vary from two inches to almost six inches long, depending on their relative success in feeding and in holding territories conducive to fast growth. Salmon fry also grow at differing rates, and there may be a benefit to the species in having this variation in the rate of development, of which more later.

The next stage in a salmonid fry's life is when it becomes a parr. The distinction between fry and parr has always been somewhat arbitrary and is loosely based on size. A young salmonid is generally deemed to be a fry or 'fingerling' while it is about the length of a man's finger. (Conventional wisdom seems not to specify which finger, still less to take account of variations in hand size!) Larger fry are referred to as parr and in salmon and sea trout these grow on to a length of anything from five to nine inches before they enter the next, very important, phase of their lives – as smolts preparing for migration.

But migration is preceded by the development period in the river, from ova to smolt, which may last for as little as eighteen months or up to seven or eight years depending upon circumstances. Unless they survive this period, migration is irrelevant.

Once the post-alevin stage is reached, salmonid fry become more active in their search for food, primarily insect larvae at first, with emergent and fully developed insect items and crustaceans taken freely as the parr grow larger and more active. Large numbers of active parr lying in shallow water are conspicuous and attractive to a variety of winged preda-

40 *Salmon and trout develop through the parr stage, when they carry these distinctive thumb-print marks on their flanks. This young salmon will develop into a silvery smolt and migrate downstream to the sea, from which it will return to spawn in the river of its birth.*

tors, which include herons, cormorants, kingfishers and sawbill species like mergansers and goosanders. The extent to which these birds, most of which are now fully protected in Britain and Ireland, make a serious impact on game fish populations remains to be fully demonstrated, and more research will be necessary before the answers become clear. Although one Canadian survey estimated that approximately 1,200 mergansers on one river consumed an astonishing annual total of almost two million salmon parr, it cannot be assumed that even the most extreme control measures against any or all of these birds would actually result in significantly improved game fish stocks. Until the case against an alleged predator is clearly proved and appropriate management and control techniques developed there can be no possible justification for the destruction of protected birds. That is not to deny the real concern, repeatedly expressed, of fishery proprietors about the alleged depredations of goosanders and mergansers, especially in Scotland, and there seems to be a case for closer study of their effects on salmon and trout parr. Meanwhile, like all responsible game management, the running of fisheries must be conducted within the letter and the spirit of the law.

While brown trout continue to grow and mature within freshwater systems, those migrant sea trout and salmon parr which have survived all the hazards of river life must enter a further stage immediately prior to migration. The change from parr to smolt is marked by the assumption of a silvery coat. This usually begins to appear in early spring, when a glandular secretion called guanine starts to give a silver coating to the fish. Having hitherto occupied small individual territories while growing, the salmon and sea trout smolts now form large shoals of hundreds or thousands of fish which migrate downstream, feeding greedily as they go. They are a perennial nuisance to spring fishermen, for their voracious feeding makes them inclined to take any bait, lure or fly at this stage, and they are unlikely to survive the stresses of being hooked, handled and returned to the water, however careful the fisherman may be. However, much more serious than these individual losses is the mass destruction of smolts in shoals by hydroelectric turbines, now a feature of so many salmon and sea trout rivers in Britain and elsewhere.

Just as game of all types – furred, feathered and finned – and wildlife in general must be accommodated within an intelligently integrated system of environmental use and exploitation, there need not be conflict between the generating of electricity from flowing water and the maintenance of flourishing stocks of migratory fish. Hydroelectric installations must be designed in full knowledge of the needs of salmon and sea trout for free movement up and down the river. Since medieval times it has been the first principle of river use that the passage of salmon must not be interrupted. As hydroelectric schemes have developed there has been a growing recognition of the need to protect migrant smolts and post-spawning kelts from the intakes of turbines as the fish drop downstream, and to provide fish passes and ladders to aid their upstream progress. On balance the former is the more important, as fish moving upstream will try various routes until they find one which is unblocked. Smolts and kelts dropping down the river may have no second chance. Earlier attitudes tended to ignore the mass destruction of fish in turbines and to make a gesture by creating artificial hatcheries to make good the damage, but a wiser and more natural approach has emerged. Why destroy fish and be put to the expense of setting up hatcheries which will be costly and of doubtful long-term value to game fish populations when a little more thought and care in the design of hydro installations can largely avoid the problem?

The fundamental principle is to position the turbine intakes at ninety degrees to the main flow of the water with a free passage for fish which can continue on their way directly downstream. The aim must always be to provide as natural and unimpeded a downstream lead as possible, and at all costs to avoid a situation where sheer weight of water smashes the fish against grids intended for their protection, or pulls them through and into the turbines. Much has been achieved since the Second World War in the design of fish passes and their intelligent incorporation into hydro schemes can minimise the effect on salmon and sea trout. But bitter memories still linger of whole river systems almost destroyed by earlier schemes. Two such examples from Ireland make the point, where the Shannon's abundant salmon stocks were so severely depleted after the Ardnacrusha hydro station was built. The Erne system which empties into the Atlantic was once one of Europe's most productive salmon fisheries. Today the Ballyshannon power station has made the catching of a salmon a rare event in a river system where before the war anglers could regularly take a dozen spring fish to one rod in a morning.

But, to return to an earlier point, why do migrant salmonids display such differences in smolting age? The first limiting factor seems to be size, and parr will not become smolts until they reach a length of at least five inches. Most smolts are between five and seven inches when they leave the river, and there is thus a direct link between food availability and the length of the growing season on the one hand and the age at which parr grow big enough to become smolts. Salmon parr from south-country chalk streams like the Frome in Dorset and the Avon and the Test in Hampshire may almost all be ready to become smolts and migrate at the age of fifteen or sixteen months — that is, as yearlings. Scotland's most northerly rivers, however, produce 60 per cent or so of their smolts after three years, and on the very limits of the Atlantic salmon's range in northern Norway many parr may be seven or eight years old before they first go to sea.

Research has revealed an inverse relationship between smolt age and the age at which salmon return to spawn in their home river. The smolt which leaves the Hampshire Avon as a yearling may make its first return after several years at sea as a 20- or 30-pound fish, while two- or three-year old smolts from a west Highland river return after one sea-winter as grilse weighing perhaps 5 or 6 pounds. A yearling smolt which returns as a grilse is quite exceptional while the 40-pounder of which an angler's dreams are made will almost always have gone to sea after one year.

For parr hatched in the same river from one year's spawning to develop at different rates and to migrate over a period of two or three years is probably a natural means of helping to protect the species against the devastating mortality which might occur if some disaster overtook a population of young fish which all matured and migrated simultaneously. Similarly, return runs of grilse and mature salmon spread over a number of years should make a population more secure against some calamity which might befall a river system.

Overwhelmingly violent spates, severe droughts, heat-waves creating temporarily overheated de-oxygenated water, and the effects of temporary pollution are potentially very serious blows to the river and loch habitats of salmon and sea trout, but the staggered migration and return pattern of these

species helps buffer local populations against such even-
tualities. Migratory game fish have survived these local
dramas for aeons: infinitely more serious is the relentless
destruction of freshwater habitat, continually growing rates
of acidification, riverbed silting and compaction and pollution from agricultural and industrial sources, to which must
be added the more recent overexploitation of salmon at sea,
both on their deep-sea feeding grounds and while returning
to the rivers of their birth. These are all in varying degrees
destructive of our migratory game fish and they are all caused
by man. Human pressures are combining to put the Atlantic
salmon under an intolerable threat and, if the species is to
survive, these pressures must be reduced and removed
wherever possible.

About a century ago the great Victorian fisheries expert
and salmon enthusiast Frank Buckland wrote about the
hazards and vicissitudes which beset salmon throughout
their life-cycle. His amusingly anthropomorphic account is
worth quoting at some length:

Perhaps the most unfortunate thing in the world is the
salmon. Everybody and everything, from the otter to the
fisherman, persecutes him. He is naturally an inhabitant of
the sea. He runs up the rivers, and would almost jump into
the pot on the kitchen fire if allowed, but every effort is put
forth to keep him at a distance. He gets fat in the sea,
though what his food is nobody quite knows. He is in the
habit, however, of going up the rivers to his country
quarters in the mountains, along with his wife and family.
Then almost at the outset, he is caught by a seal lying in
wait for him, as in the Tay, for instance. Then comes a net,
then a weir, and next a steamer frightens him back; then
the refuse from the town forces him to choose between
returning and being poisoned. The weirs across rivers are
the main cause why our fisheries have fallen off; yet all that
is wanted is a fish ladder, a series of steps or boxes
extending up over the weir.

If the salmon succeeds in leaping the weir, he next meets

with an angler, who may however fail to hook him; then on arriving at his proposed destination, he encounters the poacher, who tries to spear him with a trident. Escaping him, the salmon at last reach their breeding place, where Mistress Salmon begins stirring the gravel with her tail, and making a hollow nest lays her eggs. . . . The trout then comes to eat the eggs; next a whole swarm of flies and insects; then the water ouzel, who goes to eat the flies, is shot by ourselves, under the idea that the bird is after the eggs, and not after the flies. Other enemies come: the jack, and the otter who follows the little salmon on their way to the sea, where the angler-fish lies in wait for them. The result is that not one egg in ten thousand becomes food for man.

To Buckland's acute and succinct summary of the risks and threats to salmon survival we must now add new and more menacing developments.

'Where do salmon go at sea?' Until recently that was *the* great unanswered question about the species, whose marine activities and movements have been a great mystery over which fishermen and naturalists have puzzled for centuries. Salmon enthusiasts have always wanted to know more about the life-cycle of the species and the greatest gap in our knowledge has always been the sea phase. It is only natural to want to have the fullest understanding of a much-loved species. But some, more prophetic than they realised, saw the potential dangers for the species if its life at sea and the whereabouts of its marine feeding grounds became known, for high-seas fishing and the consequent risk of overexploitation for quick profits would be bound to develop.

That knowledge developed in the post-war period with the large-scale tagging of smolts about to migrate to sea and also of kelts, spent adult fish tagged after spawning and before they returned to the sea. Gradually there emerged an increasingly clear pattern which revealed that the North Atlantic to the west and south of Greenland was a major focus for salmon originating in the rivers of the British Isles. As more data became available this fact became more apparent and more widely known, and other modern technological developments helped to confirm the importance of these waters for salmon. Sonar and other echo location techniques revealed the presence of large shoals of fish and the development of nylon monofilament netting, almost invisible to fish, provided a new means of exploitation which is deadly in its effectiveness.

So the great mystery of the salmon's whereabouts at sea was solved – or partially so, for there may be other salmon areas in the Atlantic which are as yet unknown. But with the discovery of the Greenland fishery and, by a simple process of deduction, the migration routes of salmon returning to the river of their birth there dawned the most potentially destructive era in the long history of the salmon's struggle for survival against all the other age-old odds so well expressed by Buckland.

Each maritime nation sets its territorial limits and exercises a more or less effective degree of jurisdiction over its offshore waters. But the high seas are infinitely less easy to legislate for and to police. There was, and still is, virtually nothing effective which can be done to stop the large-scale use of monofilament nets to take salmon in international waters. The rule of law on the oceans of the world is largely a matter of international consensus, whether we are talking about piracy, whaling or salmon fishing. The degree of international agreement and co-operation necessary to avoid overexploitation of the Atlantic salmon at sea does not yet exist, although the situation is less anarchic than it was a decade or more ago. Deep-sea boats, each fishing with several miles of monofilament drift net or long-lines, can catch prodigious numbers of salmon, and it is the nature of monofilament to damage those fish which may struggle free to such an extent that they are unlikely to survive. With modern vessels equipped to stay at sea and fish actively for months, storing their catches in ice or trans-shipping at sea to 'mother ships' (perhaps of other nations) with cold storage facilities, the means of overexploitation now exist, and the market price of salmon, though relatively lower than it used to be, still makes it a very profitable activity. To the effects of deep-sea fishing must also be added offshore drift-netting, which can intercept returning salmon en route for their natal rivers.

Nations like Britain, Norway, Canada and the United States share a common heritage in the Atlantic salmon and it is in the river systems of these and other countries that the salmon begin and complete their life-cycles of birth and spawning. The natural desire among these salmon-producing countries is to protect their stocks by maintaining a sensible level of exploitation of what, if properly managed, is a renewable natural resource. The recently formed North Atlantic Salmon Conservation Organisation seeks to provide these nations with a forum for the discussion and study of the species and the safeguarding of its best interests by pressing for such measures as limiting of high-seas and offshore netting and the setting of quotas for salmon harvesting. But conservationists and sportsmen in Britain and Ireland are concerned at the way in which our interests are represented in NASCO, since we have no direct voice but are represented by the European Economic Community as a whole. But Britain and Ireland are the only salmon-producing nations of any consequence in the EEC, while other member states like Denmark with its Faroese fishery are often regarded as major offenders when it comes to overexploitation by sea fishing.

These doubts were reiterated as this chapter was being written, when the House of Lords debated the second reading of Viscount Thurso's private District Salmon Fisheries (Scotland) Bill on 19 February 1985. Almost without exception the speakers condemned the excesses of high-seas drift-netting and long-lining and singled out the Greenland and Faroese fisheries for special criticism. The interception of salmon on their return migration, though somewhat reduced since the 1970s, is still seen as a major threat to the future of salmon in Britain and Ireland, especially when it is carried out by fishing fleets from nations which have no salmon rivers and thus make no contribution to salmon production.

Such countries are naturally seen as profiteering by harvesting the crop sown by others, and as having no long-term concern or responsibility for the conservation of the species. Canada has recently imposed severe restrictions on its own harvest of salmon, both by commercial and sporting fishing, and urged that the West Greenland Commission, one of the three regional commissions which NASCO comprises, should adopt a quota of 310 tonnes of salmon for the West Greenland fishery in 1984. This was the declared total catch for the 1983 season, against an allowable quota of 1,190 tonnes. The United States voted in favour of the Canadian proposal but it was vetoed by the EEC, the third member of the commission. It is alleged that the EEC's action was instigated by Denmark, which represents the interests of the Faroese government in the EEC, since the Faroese fishermen were not prepared to reduce their quota of 625 tonnes despite pressure that they should do so in NASCO's North East Atlantic Commission.

At a subsequent meeting of the West Greenland Commission in July 1984 the necessary unanimous vote was given to a quota of 870 tonnes for the 1984 season which began in August. There was widespread disquiet at the Faroese issue being allowed to affect the decisions of the West Greenland Commission, and the Faroese came in for further attack in the North East Atlantic Commission, within whose area its offshore fisheries lie. Iceland asked for an end to salmon fishing outside a 12-mile limit around the Faroes and a total ban on drift nets. Norway urged the reduction of the Faroese quota from 625 to 500 tonnes but this was not achieved.

Nevertheless, the West Greenland Commission's reduced quota of 870 tonnes was regarded as a major step forward and hailed by many as a turning point for the Atlantic salmon after years of overexploitation. The Atlantic Salmon Trust, one of a number of organisations concerned with the problem, took the view that this restraint might mean an additional 50,000 mature multi-sea-winter salmon, chiefly females, returning to spawn in European rivers. Time will tell whether this estimate is correct, and much more restraint in high-seas exploitation may still be needed before the spring runs of large multi-sea-winter fish are restored in British and Irish rivers.

Overexploitation is by no means the monopoly of other nations. The offshore fishing activities of England and Ireland are both under widespread criticism and attack in many well informed quarters. Illegal fishing with monofilament drift nets off the west coast of Ireland has reached such proportions that the situation is now regarded as out of control, a free-for-all which is alleged to have accounted for as many as 300,000 salmon, chiefly grilse, in 1984 alone. This overfishing was attacked in the Lords debate just mentioned, but particularly harsh criticism was reserved for English east-coast drift netting.

It is known that a high proportion of the salmon heading for the great classic rivers of Scotland's east coast, like the Tweed, Tay, Dee and Spey, pass northwards up the east coast of England. But there is extensive offshore drift-netting from the Wash up to the Scottish border at Berwick upon Tweed from 1 April onwards. It is a strange irony that this drift-net interception of fish returning to Scottish rivers was outlawed off the Scottish coast by the Sea Fish (Conservation) Act 1967, but continues unabated in English offshore waters. It is alleged that 95 per cent of salmon taken by this fishery are heading for Scottish rivers, and those are the fish which have already escaped the depredations of high-seas netting. It is almost universally regarded as placing an intolerable strain on runs of salmon to east-coast Scottish rivers, where the spring runs of larger multi-sea-winter fish have almost disappeared.

The regulating and policing of high-seas fishing remains difficult, but this east-coast drift-netting is under the control of English fishery boards and ultimately of British legislation. Salmon conservationists, sportsmen and organisations like the Atlantic Salmon Trust are united in their belief that the Northumbrian drift-net fishing should be banned forthwith, or at the very least restricted and controlled much more strictly, preparatory to its total phasing out. There is general agreement that this would be the greatest single step towards restoring runs of salmon, especially in spring, and improving spawning success in the greatest remaining salmon rivers of the British Isles. If our stocks of salmon and sea trout are lost from these rivers, the last major strongholds of migratory game fish in Britain, it will be the final nail in the coffin. Unless the north-east English coastal fishery is severely restricted or removed altogether, that fate seems inevitable.

The final netting hazards to be negotiated by salmon are the systems of shoreline and estuarine netting, most of which operate under licence from the river boards and are controlled or heavily influenced by the owners of the upstream rod fisheries; and the illegal netting and poisoning activities of poachers. Poaching, especially on a large-scale commercial basis, is an ever-present problem in Scotland and Ireland, and its prevention is directly related to the manpower which private fishery owners and the police can make available. As long as there is a ready sale for illegally taken salmon to dishonest game dealers, and to hotels and caterers prepared to buy fish at the back door without asking too many questions, this seems likely to continue. Night-surveillance equipment and walkie-talkie radios are used not only by the more organised estates in patrolling and guarding their waters; they are also the tools of the commercial poacher's trade, which combines an ever-increasing degree of technological sophistication with an alarming amount of intimidation and violence towards water bailiffs, gamekeepers and their families. Perhaps some system of tagging, such as is used in Canada, may help to make the trade in illegally taken salmon more difficult, but there is no obvious way to stop it completely. To ban the sale of all salmon would be impossible, and undesirable, as it would wipe out legitimate and intelligent harvesting of a renewable resource.

The development since the 1960s of salmon farming in sea cages has progressed by leaps and bounds. The deeply indented, well sheltered sea lochs of Scotland's west coast seem particularly well suited to this activity, which is providing an increasing volume of salmon for the commercial market each year. Its efficiency and profitability are steadily increasing, and it has been welcomed as a major way of supplying the commercial demand for salmon without making undue inroads into the wild stock. But the possibility of serious disease developing among fish ranched in large numbers and closely confined in sea cages and the risk of infection of the wild fish is a constant concern, as are the possible consequences of experimental genetic manipulation of captive-bred salmon to improve their food-conversion performance, increase fish-farm output and produce a more profitable product. While ranched salmon may have a key role to play in easing the pressures on our overexploited wild fish, those involved in the organisation and development of these schemes bear a heavy responsibility to ensure that the health and genetic integrity of wild fish populations are not disrupted.

Perhaps the growing of captive salmon in this way can be developed both as a means of supplying the commercial demand for salmon and also to provide employment for those currently making a living as netsmen in the river estuaries and along the Scottish firths. Depleted runs of fish into the rivers have reduced the annual netting harvest and this has inevitably been followed by demands from netsmen that the netting season should be adjusted to enable them to catch running fish at the best times of the year. The alternative, they point out, is for netting to become less and less economically viable and eventually to disappear. To change the seasons and allow netting to be timed to catch the remaining salmon runs is generally regarded as a potentially disastrous course of action. Few enough salmon succeed in returning to spawn as things are: to change the netting seasons in this way would be more than salmon stocks could bear, and it has been rejected on several rivers already. To net in such a way as to hit hard at the remaining runs of salmon is to eat the seed corn of future years – a short-term policy which might keep netsmen in employment for a few more seasons but would eliminate the salmon completely, and probably permanently. Where are we to place our priorities in deciding

such questions? Are jobs and policies of short-term expedi-
ency to take precedence over the very survival of migratory
fish in our river systems?

The rivers of Scotland and Ireland, and the relatively few
English and Welsh rivers which still sustain sizeable salmon
stocks, are under quite unprecedented environmental and
commercial pressure in a host of ways, some of which have
been discussed. But what of the rod fisherman? The sporting
angler sees the salmon not as a source of financial gain but as
a coveted prize to be pursued with enthusiasm and skill, with
the odds loaded heavily in favour of the fish, and at a cost
which may amount to hundreds of pounds for a week's
fishing on a classic beat. Does sporting fishing constitute
another pressure on our salmon? Should we impose daily or
weekly bag limits on fishermen in the British Isles? These
questions are now being debated by salmon conservationists,
many of whom are keen anglers and understand the self-
restraint which they may have to impose upon their own
sporting activities. It is a tribute to the sportsmen's sense of
responsibility and their affection for the species they pursue
that their thoughts should tend in this direction. It would be
enormously heartening to see commercial fishermen taking a
leaf out of their book.

The demand for game fishing of quality, for trout and
salmon, is growing and represents another aspect of the ever-
increasing demand for recreation in the countryside. More
leisure and the genuine need for the office worker and city
dweller to escape and enjoy relaxation and recreation in the
open air means that fishing is a growing sport. Like other
field sports and country activities it entails additional pressures on our countryside and its wildlife. And, sadly for the
townsman, the finest wild game fish now live in rivers, lakes
and lochs far away from our centres of population. Man has
no one but his own species to blame for this – his polluting
ancestors and contemporaries have seen to that. But our
expanding understanding of fish biology and fish culture has
enabled us to develop purpose-designed fisheries to provide
sport for the game fisherman, and to create amenities and

41 *The rainbow trout was introduced to Britain from its native North America a century ago, and in the last thirty years this species has revolutionised the management of many game fisheries, especially on stillwaters. The rainbow trout has a rapid growth rate and is particularly suitable for new man-made lakes and reservoirs. Genetic manipulation has enabled hatcheries to produce well-conditioned, silvery fish with fine sporting qualities, like this magnificent 13¼ pound specimen from a Hampshire fishery.*

opportunities for recreation in reservoirs, gravel pits and other artificial waterways.

Pre-eminent in this has been the rainbow trout (*S. gairdneri*) which, in the rivers and lakes of North America west of the Mississippi, fills approximately the same niche as the brown trout in Europe. (Like the brown trout with its migratory brother, the sea trout, the rainbow too has an anadromous form, the steelhead.) The first batch of ova from this New World species was hatched at the Howietown hatchery of Sir James Maitland in 1885, and there began an undreamt-of new development which was to transform the game fishing scene in the British Isles. The rainbow's great attraction is the various advantages it offers to the fishery manager and the commercial fish farmer compared with the brown trout. It is an especially good food converter, turning its fish-farm diet of nutrient pellets into protein and growing into a good sporting fish at a much faster rate than the brown trout. It grows quickly even in crowded conditions and if it has fed well it is as delicious a table fish as any of the salmonid species. It will tolerate higher water temperatures than brown trout and continues to feed and provide sport in the height of summer, when the warmth of the dog days causes brown trout to sulk dourly in the cooler depths of rivers and lakes, almost uncatchable for the fly-fisher.

It has had a bad press, however, on several counts. It rises less freely than the brown trout; its wandering nature makes it more manageable in lakes, reservoirs and other stillwaters than in rivers; it will not breed as readily as the brown trout; and there are accounts of the disagreeably black and slimy appearance of male fish in spring and the frequently tatty looks of stocked fish reared in overcrowded concrete stew-ponds. But, on balance, the rainbow has been a great success, especially in the post-war period, which has seen a massive expansion of the species. This falls into two broad categories: the farming of rainbows to supply a growing public demand for trout in restaurants and on the family table; and the development of sporting game fisheries, chiefly in stillwaters. There is an inevitable degree of overlap, since many hatcheries and fish farms supply fish direct to fishmongers and hoteliers, and also to sporting fishery managers for their stocking requirements.

The expansion of cities and towns and their attendant industries has meant a great increase in demand for water, for domestic and industrial purposes. The creation of new reservoirs like Rutland Water and Kielder has provided Britain with vast new stillwaters, often within easy reach of major centres of population. These fulfil their primary purpose of providing water, and as a spin-off they present all kinds of opportunities for recreation. The yachtsman, wind-surfer and water-skier have benefited, but these water sports are overshadowed by the huge demand for and interest in stillwater trout fishing. This provides an enormous amount of fun and relaxation for tens of thousands of fishermen – a survey in 1981 showed that close to a million people in Great Britain go game fishing fairly regularly, and of these a high proportion depend heavily upon rainbow-stocked stillwaters for their sport.

The business of catching rainbow trout in stillwaters, large and small, has evolved its own specialised techniques and tackle, and fishery management and our understanding of fish culture has developed too. The management of rainbow trout fisheries is a matter of 'put and take', with judicious stocking of hatchery-bred fish replacing nature's cycle of spawning and regeneration. Having acknowledged that basic fact, and realising that the game fisherman on heavily fished stillwaters is paying to catch attractive, sporting fish, there have been moves to produce a 'product' which fills those requirements, by techniques of selective breeding and genetic manipulation.

It is now regular practice to stock rainbow stillwaters with a fish which is female in its physical characteristics but quite sterile – technically known as a triploid. This is a genetically engineered variant which never comes into spawning condition or undergoes any mating urge, remaining clean and silvery-bright all year round. Ample food and optimum water temperatures will promote quick growth, thereby fulfilling the twin demands for big fish which can be caught to provide good sport and fine eating all year round. Whatever you may think of this tampering with fish genetics to develop an essentially artificial product, there is no denying that they supply a sporting demand and this in turn helps to take the pressure off our wild stocks of native brown trout and migratory salmonids, which would otherwise be subjected to excessive fishing pressure and general disturbance. It also means that a great many vast, manmade waters and tiny ponds which would otherwise be virtually lifeless now enjoy populations of game fish and can offer much-needed sport for growing numbers of people.

It must never be forgotten that so-called 'artificial' fish management has brought about some enormous advances in our understanding of fish biology and genetics – knowledge which can be ploughed back into the critical fight to retain and safeguard our heritage of wild game fish, so severely depleted by man's thoughtless and wanton destruction of their environment but not yet beyond hope of recovery, if our knowledge and technical skills in fishery and environmental management can be matched by the *will* to save our game fish for future generations.

14. *A Future for Game?*

Among all the game species which have been discussed here, only the deer and to a lesser degree the woodcock are expanding their populations and significantly extending their range. All the others are, to a greater or lesser extent, in decline. Some, like the grey partridge and the black grouse, are in serious trouble as wild populations dwindle to a tiny fraction of what they used to be. The plight of Scotland's red grouse poses a very real threat to the economic viability of many upland areas, to the employment which it has hitherto provided in some of Britain's most remote rural communities, and thus to the maintenance of a unique upland ecological system. Overexploitation of our salmon at sea and the degradation and destruction of their river habitat have already virtually wiped out the main spring runs of adult fish into what used to be our best rivers and reduced their production of new generations of salmon and trout.

This generally bleak picture is made all the more distressing by the fact that we can now explain many of the reasons why these declines have occurred and can propose effective measures to help remedy the situation. Yet the declines continue. What future is there for our game species?

The answer is not a simple one, for wild game cannot be viewed in isolation but must be seen in the broader context of wildlife and land use in the British Isles in general. Farmers and landowners are under pressure as never before to strive for maximum productivity and cost-effectiveness, whether their land is grazed by livestock, cropped for cereals or planted with commercial timber. This drive for ever-increasing yields has led to gross overproduction of many commodities, resulting in large-scale intervention measures and guaranteed subsidies to bolster up a situation which would otherwise have reached crisis point long ago. Over-production has been made possible by a ruthlessly efficient and often very blinkered approach to land use, aided by recent advances in agricultural and forestry technology. Large monocultures, as in the vast new cereal fields of the arable lowlands or the great even-aged forests of non-native conifers on our poorer upland soils, have been established where formerly there was a diversity of crops and a mosaic of semi-natural self-seeded vegetation, interspersed with areas of arable crops, grassland and, in upland areas, large acreages of heather. That vanishing landscape was rich in game and wildlife of all kinds, but the simplification of arable cropping and the tidying up of the countryside has militated against many species of wildlife, especially when radical changes in land use have been compounded by the effects of agro-chemical sprays and other agents which, while they may benefit the Sitka spruce trees or the wheat crop, may decimate many other species of plants and insects. This in turn can have a knock-on effect by reducing the survival rate of insect-dependent game bird chicks such as partridges and black-game, and there are other repercussions for butterflies, songbirds, wild flowers and many other species as well.

An additional factor in this complex equation is the way in which the long-predicted growth in demand for recreational and leisure access to the countryside has developed. Increasing numbers of leisured and highly mobile urban-based people are turning to the countryside for a much-needed and important source of physical and mental refreshment for those whose lives are lived in the rush and bustle of cities or in sedentary Monday-to-Friday jobs. Their legitimate needs must also be accommodated in any future strategy for the best use of our precious and finite rural resources.

The last few years have seen the emergence of an important and expanding 'environment industry', and an unparalleled growth of interest by the man in the street in the natural world, promoted and mirrored by more and more television and radio coverage of wildlife and environmental matters, and the publication of many more books and periodicals about animals, plants and birds. Never before has the general public been so intensely interested in and well informed about many environmental issues, and all the indications are that this trend will develop further and become a significant political influence in the future, as is already the case in some other European countries.

The passage of the Wildlife and Countryside Act 1981 provided clear evidence of the intense interest which exists in conservation and the environment. The unprecedentedly large number of amendments which were tabled, and the amount of parliamentary time which was devoted to the discussion of this legislation, is striking proof of the depth of feeling and the passionate concern felt by many politicians, who reflect the often opposing interests and views of a wide range of groups and organisations.

How does game fit into this complex scene? Our game birds, fish and mammals are just one part of the much wider wildlife scene, but the ecological interaction of species in the environment means that everyone who wishes to secure a future for all our wildlife must seek to create a balance, to devise an integrated approach to the ways in which we use our countryside so as to fulfil all the many and growing demands that are made upon it. We must avoid the 'tunnel vision' which can result from the exclusive pursuit of any one aspect of land use, and adopt a broader attitude. The Victorian gamekeeper who waged an obsessive war against 'vermin' – by which he meant almost every creature which was not game – failed to take that wider view of wildlife in general, and so the old style of gamekeepering got a bad name among naturalists, and rightly so. It was a blinkered attitude to game management which stemmed largely from ignorance, and the gamekeeper of the 1980s is infinitely better informed and has a wider, wiser and more sympathetic understanding of wildlife in general.

But if a modern forester designs a vast new plantation without regard for the appearance of the landscape and the well-being of wildlife he is just as culpable as was the Victorian gamekeeper with his 'vermin gibbet' and may do more serious long-term damage to wildlife. There is more to forestry than simply the production of timber and, while that may be the principal aim in planting a new forest, the forester must not lose sight of the wider environmental implications of what he is doing. Likewise the arable farmer must not be motivated solely by the desire for ever more efficient ways of producing higher crop yields. Spraying, while necessary, should not be undertaken without regard to wildlife. The hedges and small woodlands which he may be tempted to pull out, to allow his large machines to manoeuvre more easily, are vital habitat not only for game but for scores of other creatures and many varieties of plants and wild flowers.

If the private forester or the farmer is a sportsman then he is much more likely to take into account the needs of game. Hedges and copses will be retained and maintained and new areas of game habitat may be planted, and the principal motivation for all this is game shooting. Much of the British landscape has been moulded and shaped by the tree planting and habitat management of earlier sporting generations, and that tradition continues today. Game may be the principal motivation, but all wildlife benefits in the end. Many a sporting farmer only retains a hedge or a belt of trees because of its value to his shoot. It may even be a considerable agricultural nuisance but it is kept and maintained for the sport it affords – and when the songbirds nest there and the butterflies and wild flowers flourish in summer that is an added bonus, for what began as a sporting asset has become a generally important wildlife amenity. The same is true of small, newly planted woodlands of only an acre or two – useless in terms of timber production and established solely for their sporting potential. This creates new game habitat, provides better sport, enhances the capital value of the sporting side of the farm and probably generates an annual income from sporting rents far above that which could be expected from any purely commercial crop. And when such places are colonised by other creatures these game spinneys make a real contribution to wildlife conservation in general.

The upland proprietor has traditionally relied upon a combination of hill sheep farming and grouse shooting to give him an income from his moorland acres. By following this path and managing the heather with grouse in mind he has also maintained an environment which benefits many other species of upland birds, and the important contribution of grouse moor management to the ecological well-being of the uplands is generally acknowledged by environmentalists. But if grouse decline to the point where the traditional combination of grouse and sheep is no longer economically viable, the owners will inevitably be forced to opt for one of the two principal alternatives, of intensive hill sheep farming or conifer afforestation, which enjoy attractive subsidies, grants and tax concessions. By maintaining our moors for grouse we also retain a suitable environment for many other upland species.

Most land in Britain is still in private ownership, and that can be both a blessing and something of a disadvantage for wildlife. An integrated, country-wide land-use policy would appear, on the face of it, to be easier to implement if all land were under some degree of centralised control. At present, one landowner may work his land thoughtfully and to the benefit of game and other wildlife while his neighbour pursues a blinkered policy of high-yield farming without regard for the environment. This lack of uniformity presents

42 *The prairie farming landscape of much of lowland Britain has meant the loss of vital habitat for game and other creatures. Fieldsports often provide the principal motivation for leaving a hedgerow or small woodland which would otherwise be pulled out. A landscape rich in wild game is also home for a wide variety of other birds, plants and insects.*

environmentalists with an important challenge and the problem is principally an educational one, to persuade the agricultural profiteer of the short-sightedness of his policies.

But the benefits of private ownership of land and the sporting rights over it far outweigh any administrative advantages which in the view of some commentators might result from nationalisation or some other form of centralised ownership of land. The private landowner has, in general, proved himself to be a responsible custodian of his land and the wildlife it sustains, and his control of the sporting rights means that game and other wildlife are protected from undue pressure. This is only to be expected when an individual wishes to enjoy the sporting amenities of his land without jeopardising the future of his wild game stocks. If a salmon beat is only fished on a certain number of weeks each year, if a moor is only shot over on certain agreed days, and if deer are stalked and shot in accordance with a careful management plan, disturbance is kept to a minimum and a harvest of game can be taken with only minimal disruption to wildlife and the environment.

Unchecked public access and uncontrolled sporting pressures would be a disastrous and insupportable burden for game in many parts of Britain. We must learn from the experience of other countries where free public access to the land has radically upset many forms of wildlife, and where a sporting free-for-all has wrought havoc with game populations. No one will pay the wages of a gamekeeper, water bailiff or stalker if his conservation efforts are to be thwarted by a public invasion of the woods, moors or riverbanks by shooters and fishermen who have no responsibility for their actions, individual or collective, and who may do great damage to game stocks very quickly.

Excessive disturbance and overexploitation can extend to other forms of wildlife too, and the laws of trespass and the privileges of private ownership are two of the most important bastions which protect our wildlife from grossly excessive public pressures. Those who enjoy the best of our British and Irish game shooting and fishing are the ones who put the most back into game management, either by personal effort or by paying for their sport, thus enabling estates to employ river bailiffs and gamekeepers. This is in marked contrast to situations like that which arose in Portugal in the 1970s when, after the political upheavals there, many of the most productive private partridge shoots were thrown open to public shooting. Within a few years excessive disturbance, high shooting pressure and the virtual cessation of game management and predator control had almost wiped out the partridge population in areas where they once flourished. Many celebrated shoots in Portugal lost well over 90 per cent of their partridges and those are not by any means the most extreme instances of what happened. The clear message is that game and wildlife will not flourish in areas where the human population is allowed to create high levels of disturbance.

Shooting, fishing and other field sports as currently practised in the British Isles do not constitute a threat to any game species, and the best recent research confirms this. Unless some major social and political revolution changes the rural scene, field sports are not likely to produce a sudden surge of pressure to threaten our game. The true threats are more sinister and insidious, stemming from agricultural and industrial pollution, habitat loss, changing land use and the general struggle to maintain game populations when so many other activities inimical to game and wildlife enjoy high subsidies and other attractive incentives for the private landowner or the institutional land manager. It can be difficult for someone who does not shoot, fish or hunt to appreciate that those whose sporting activities result in the death of game are also the most active protectors of game species, and the most enthusiastic supporters of the game biologists and professional game managers who are seeking new ways of ensuring a future for our game. We return again to the principle of enlightened self-interest – those who are keenest in pursuit of game with rod, rifle or gun are also the most active and practical of game conservationists.

There need be no conflict between a future for game

species and the field sports which are associated with them, and other aspects of land use. If everyone who cares about our countryside, its wildlife and our heritage of wild game is prepared to be sufficiently flexible, imaginative and innovative in their approach to this challenge, game and other wildlife *can* have a secure future in a countryside where the farmer, the forester, the rambler, the field sportsman and the man who is simply going for a stroll with his dog can coexist in a harmonious and integrated use of our irreplaceable rural environment.